THE
GREAT MARCH
BOOK II

THE PUBLICATION OF THIS VOLUME
WAS MADE POSSIBLE BY THE ESTABLISH-
MENT OF A FUND FOR THE PUBLICATION
OF JEWISH RELIGIOUS SCHOOL LITERA-
TURE BY THE NATIONAL FEDERATION
OF TEMPLE SISTERHOODS

THE
GREAT MARCH

Post-Biblical Jewish Stories

BOOK II   REVISED EDITION

BY ROSE G. LURIE

ILLUSTRATIONS BY TODROS GELLER

THE UNION OF
AMERICAN HEBREW CONGREGATIONS
New York

Tenth Printing, 1955

TO MAX

WHO ALWAYS ENCOURAGED ME

TO MY BEST EFFORTS

Editor's Introduction

The Great March, Book II, is a sequel to *The Great March, Book I,* published several years ago by the Union of American Hebrew Congregations, and consists of a series of stories on post-Biblical Jewish heroes beginning with the expulsion from Spain, and ending with our own day. As the book is intended for young children the stories are written in as simple a style as possible. A definite attempt was made by the author to write these stories as they would be told to the child by the teacher in the class, or by the mother in the home. It is important that those using the book should bear this in mind. It will help them to make adequate use of the story material presented.

Too often stories in books intended for young children are abbreviated and condensed, the writers being under a mistaken impression that an abbreviated story shortened from a more expanded narrative for adults constitutes a good story for children. Actually, children need more details, more vivid and concrete writing. For this reason, the stories in this book were especially written in conversational tone, and the concreteness and vividness with which they are told should render them easy for dramatization. These stories will thus offer not only an opportunity for vitalizing history through dramatization, but will also serve as splendid material for assembly programs.

It is well for teachers using this book to remember that the chief aim in teaching Jewish stories of the post-biblical period to children in the early grades is not so much to convey information as to give inspiration. The cultivation of favorable Jewish attitudes is one of the most important aims in any such instruction. Whatever information the children may obtain should be considered quite incidental. While we expect them, as a result of the study of this book, to know some outstanding Jewish names and some important Jewish events, the primary end is that of cultivating a love for Jewish heroes, for the Jewish people, and for Jewish idealism.

Since the book was not written as a history, it was not deemed necessary to include certain historical events which though significant should not be included in a book for younger children. Good teaching practice at times dictated the omission of some events and some stories. So the author found it necessary here and there to vary the details of an historical event for the sake of dramatic effect. The object was to convey as far as possible a general impression of each hero and to develop on the part of the child a favorable attitude to him.

The author of this book has had years of experience as a teacher and as a critic teacher, especially in charge of extra-curricular activities in the schools of the Associated Talmud Torahs of Philadelphia. Some of the stories included in this book were tried out experimentally during the past year with children in the younger grades.

This book completes our series of Biblical and post-Biblical stories for the primary grades. As usual, suggestions and criticisms will be welcomed both by the author and by the editor. We trust that this book will help some of our boys and girls to develop a love for their people and a devotion to Jewish ideals.

EMANUEL GAMORAN

To the Teacher

WHILE studying at the Teachers Institute of the Jewish Theological Seminary some years ago, Miss Jeanette Morgenstern and I came to the conclusion that good stories would make effective motivation for the teaching of Jewish history. It was not, however, until 1926 when the Commission on Jewish Education invited me to write a series of stories related to post-Biblical Jewish history that I had the opportunity to carry out this objective. *The Great March, Book I,* which began with the destruction of the Temple and ended with the expulsion from Spain, was the result. From the very beginning it was intended to bring the stories up to our present day. However, my work at the Associated Talmud Torahs in Philadelphia, was such as to make this impossible until 1938, when I finally took a leave of absence for this purpose.

I experienced greater difficulty in writing the second volume of *The Great March* than in writing the first. The chief reason for this is, it seems to me, that historians frequently differ in the interpretation of some of the events of this period. In order to write a unified, dramatic story, one must have an integrated view of the subject, which in this case obviously implies a certain arbitrary and personal interpretation of the events described.

Furthermore, pedagogically speaking, it is obvious that every generation interprets the facts of history in the spirit of its own times.

With all this uncertainty in mind—how was one to proceed? After considerable reading I attempted to write the stories in a manner which would best portray the salient events of each hero as far as possible from the standpoint which, I believed, was the hero's own concept of his role in Jewish life. In certain instances where widely different views

ix

are held by historians, I attempted to convey these very uncertainties by the manner of presentation of these stories as in Sabbatai Zevi, Mordecai Manuel Noah, Schechter, etc.

In this series the basic historic facts are presented in their essential integrity. For pedagogic reasons and for reasons inherent in the story form, fictitious situations of a minor character were introduced.

A good teacher will use this material as a point of departure for motivation of the study of historic trends and movements. Thus the story of the Baal Shem Tov may well introduce the Chassidic period, the stories of Wise and Schechter may initiate a study of Reform and Conservative Movements in Judaism, and so on.

I have been told by teachers, and all personal observations confirmed the view, that more facts can be fixed, and needless to say emotionalized, by this means than by a didactic teaching of history as such. For this reason, though these stories were written specifically to follow *The Great March, Book I,* they can well be used to follow other texts which cover Jewish history up to 1492. Furthermore, a child need no longer repeat the same text book. He may now re-study the same facts in a different form. This should prove of great help to educators and administrators who are in need of review materials. In order to retain the interest which we hope the titles of the stories arouse, we do not want to indicate the personality or the topic treated right next to the title. Hence, for the teacher's information, the following is a list of the personalities portrayed in these stories: (1) Columbus—Luis de Santangel, (2) Luis de Torres, (3) Menasseh ben Israel, (4) Sabbatai Zevi, (5) Dona Gracia Mendes—Joseph Nasi, (6) Israel Baal Shem Tov, (7) Moses Mendelssohn, (8) Moses Montefiore, (9) Adolphe Cremieux, (10) Hayim Salomon, (11) Rebecca Gratz, (12) Judah Touro, (13) Mordecai Manuel Noah, (14) Isaac Mayer Wise, (15) Emma Lazarus, (16) Eliezer ben Jehudah, (17) Theodor Herzl, (18) Solomon Schechter, (19) Chaim Nachman Bialik, (20) Chaim Nachman Bialik.

                                        ROSE G. LURIE

Acknowledgments

THE preparation of this book has been a difficult task and obviously it would not have been possible were it not for those fine stand-bys: Graetz' *History of the Jews, The Jewish Encyclopedia, Encyclopedia Judaica, Jüdisches Lexikon, Ozar Yisroel* and periodicals like *Maznayim* and the *Hashiloach,* etc. Indeed, I could append a quite formidable bibliography; but scholars surely do not need it and teachers will in all likelihood not use it. However, it would be dishonest and ungrateful not to mention my indebtedness to such works as *Chaye Cremieux* by I. Elk; *Moses Mendelssohn, der Mensch und das Werk* by Bertha Badt Strauss; *Moses Mendelssohn, Critic and Philosopher* by Hermann Walter; *Dreamers of the Ghetto* by Israel Zangwill; *Isaac Mayer Wise* by David Philipson and Louis Grossman; *Bialik—His Life and Work* by Lachover; *Chaim Nachman Bialik* by Eisenberg; *Leben für ein Volk* by Benj. Klar; the diaries of Sir Moses and Lady Montefiore; *Moses Montefiore—Ein Lebensbild für jung und alt* by Eugene Wolfe; *Sir Moses Montefiore* by Lucien Wolf; *Rebecca Gratz* by Rollin Osterweis; *Major Noah* by Isaac Goldberg; *Baal Shem Tov* by S. Z. Zetzer (Yiddish) to mention only a very, very few.

I wish to acknowledge indebtedness to Deborah Pessin's *Modern Jewish Personalities,* originally issued in 1937, and since published under the title of *Giants on the Earth.*

A special debt of gratitude is due to my teacher and friend, Dr. Leo L. Honor, who not only motivated this effort, but criticized this volume in great detail. Much of this criticism I tried to meet and I feel sure that the book has been greatly improved because of it.

I wish also to express my appreciation to Mrs. M. Myer Singer for a careful reading of the manuscript and for many valuable suggestions.

Rabbi Leon Fram, Rabbi Iser L. Freund, and Rabbi David Polish of the Commission on Jewish Education, were helpful with many suggestions. Dr. Solomon Grayzel, too, should be thanked for reading part of the manuscript.

I am grateful to Dr. Joseph Reider of the Dropsie College Library for opening the stacks to me; and to his assistant, Miss Helen Solomon, who was most helpful not only in locating dusty source books, but also in obtaining books from other libraries. The students at Dropsie suggested an occasional good source. Last, but not least, I wish to thank Dr. David Alexander Cooper and Dr. Emanuel Gamoran, who always encouraged me in my endeavor.

R. G. L.

Table of Contents

xiv   CONTENTS

Illustrations

THE
GREAT MARCH
BOOK II

To the Reader

In following the Jews through *The Great March* we found that Spain, the land they had cherished and helped to build up, the land they had learned to love as home, began to look upon them as a burden, and ordered them to leave its shores forever. Once more they were uprooted—once more they were forced to take up the Great March. Whither?

Where were they going? Who would shelter them now? Was there a place left in all the wide world where they could take refuge? Dared the Jews hope for more miracles?

Those who could pay their way might go to Holland, Turkey or Africa. But most of them could not pay, for they had no money, no possessions. Spain, the country which was driving them out, had taken everything they had. Now suddenly, these Jews who had thought there was no way out, found cause for hope. A group of men was setting out to discover a shorter route to India. "Perhaps," thought these exiled Spanish Jews, "perhaps there we shall find a home!"

Curiously enough, this voyage to India began in the very year when the Jews in Spain were being driven from the homes they loved.

The Great March goes on!

Across the Sea

"Look, look! There goes a man with his coat full of holes."
"And see the funny red hair with streaks of grey!" The shouts
and jeers of the children followed Christopher Columbus as he
hurried to the palace of Ferdinand and Isabella, the king and
queen of Spain. Soon Columbus stood before the king pleading:

"O King and Queen, after much thinking I have come to
believe that the earth is round, and if the earth is round I can
find a new route to India by going westward." Columbus' eyes
sparkled as he continued, "With your help I can find a new and
shorter route to this land, so rich in spices, silks and gold.
Through my discovery, Spain shall become the greatest, the
richest country in the world."

He paused. Isabella and Ferdinand sat as still as two statues.
At last Isabella spoke, in a slow, hard voice: "To travel on the
Sea of Darkness is too great a risk even if the trip would bring
us more money for our wars."

4

"Besides," and King Ferdinand seemed to be getting interested, "what would you expect for yourself as your reward for the discovery?"

Columbus, who seemed to have thought it all out before, answered quickly, "I shall be Lord of the Seas, and I shall want a tenth of all the gold and precious metals that I may find."

"That's asking too much," the King replied angrily. "We should have to buy the ships, outfit them, pay the wages of your crew—and all for something that may not even exist. Who can tell what may happen?"

Columbus' face fell. The sparkle left his eyes. His whole body seemed to shrink. He couldn't argue with the King and Queen. That simply is not done! He began to gather up his maps and charts, almost ready to give up the whole idea.

Then suddenly, Luis de Santangel, the Chancellor of Spain, a Marrano (that is a Jew who made believe he was a Christian), spoke up:

"O King and Queen, if you will allow me, I will lend this money to Columbus. I love Spain and it would make me happy to see it grow rich and powerful. Besides, we may find many people who would be saved for Christianity."

Ferdinand gasped with surprise. "That's quite a different matter—quite a different matter," he said. "Of course you have our consent, and the plans may go forward at once."

No time was lost. Three little sailing vessels—the Nina, the Pinta and the Santa Maria—were made ready. But who would

man the ships? Who would risk his life for a few coins? Surely
not the people who were safe and happy at home. Then who
would be willing to go? Only those who were in debt, and
wanted to be excused from paying their debts; or convicts who
would be allowed to go free. They volunteered to go.

But there was still another group—people who were not
convicts, nor in debt. They were the Marranos, those Jews who
lived outwardly as Catholics, but secretly as Jews. They decided
to take the chance even at the risk of their lives, for they hoped
to find a refuge, a home not only for themselves but also for all
the Jewish refugees.

At last the day came—a warm, sultry day. It was August 3,
1492, at 8:00 o'clock in the morning, when the three little ships
stood ready. (August 2 was the 9th of Ov, the day on which
the First and Second Temples were destroyed.) Who were the
crew? Some were men in search of a new route to India, the
richest country in the world. Some just hungered for adventure.
Others were escaping from prison, and the Marranos were seek-
ing a haven for the oppressed Jews.

Would Columbus reach his destination? Would the oppressed Jews find a new home? Who could tell?

*   *   *

Soon there was a hustle and bustle. Three small ships were
making ready for the sea. All hands were busy. The sails were
rigged. Hurried commands were given:

Single up!
Single up!
Is Alfonso de la Calle here?
Roderigo Sanchez?—Good.
Maestro Bernal
And Marco the Surgeon?

Yes. All answered the roll call. The crew took their places. "Cast off!" was the command. The anchor was lifted. The sails filled and the ships glided out to sea. From the Santa Maria, the vessel which carried Columbus and the Jews, came the song:

> * We will reach the east,
> Though we are westward bound.
> East will bring you west
> Because the earth is round.
>
> That the earth is round
> You surely all must know
> For from his travels wide
> Columbus taught us so.

Thus the sailors sang as the ships struck out to sea.

Suddenly a shocking sight met their eyes—a ship—and people being set adrift! "Who are they? Who are they?" one after another cried. The ship they saw carried Jewish passen-

* May be sung to the tune of "Whistle While You Work" from *Snow White,* or the "Song of the Volga Boatmen."

gers who were on their way to Holland. But, after the ship had started out, it was found that some Jews on board had no money with which to pay for their passage. It was they who were cruelly set adrift at sea. Alas, there was no singing, no happy laughter on that ship.

The Jews among the crew on board the smaller ships looked on and pitied, but alas, they knew they could not help. A sad, deep silence fell upon them. Presently one man broke the stillness. He said huskily, "If we had not made believe that we were Christians, we too might be adrift in that ocean."

The Jews huddled closer together. Another remarked drearily, "And we, whither are we bound? Who knows whether this man Columbus is the right sort of leader? After all, he's just a sailor—an adventurer!"

"Don't say such foolish things," rebuked Gabriel Sanchez, once the chief treasurer of Aragon in Spain. (He too was a Marrano, for all the Marranos were on this boat.) "This man Columbus has made many voyages, and studied many maps. Abraham Zacuto, a very learned Jewish astronomer, prepared an almanac for his use on this voyage."

"Yes, an almanac," said another. "But of what use is that if we have nothing but the stars to guide us—and then only on cloudless nights?"

They were passing the Volcano of Teneriffe which gave forth a cloud of smoke by day, and a pillar of fire by night. The crew looked frightened.

Alfonso Caballeria changed the subject. "The pity is," he said, "that though the Jews are being driven out of Spain, it is they who made this voyage possible. It is they who made the maps and the instruments with which to navigate the sea."

"That may be true," said another, "but if the Queen had not pawned the jewels from her crown, Columbus would not have had the money with which to buy those instruments, nor even the ships with which to make the voyage."

Here Luis de Torres, another Marrano, interrupted him angrily. "The queen's jewels, indeed," he said mockingly. "Luis de Santangel, Chancellor of the royal household in Spain, helped to make this voyage possible."

De Torres leaned back in his chair looking longingly toward the land which they were leaving behind, the land in which he had grown up, and which he loved above all others.

He was thinking sadly, "I may never see my country again," when a group of men appeared.

"Luis de Torres! Luis de Torres!" they clamoured. "Speak! Who did supply the money for this voyage? How did it all happen?"

"Columbus came to the court in Spain after trying to convince the court in Portugal and said he could find a new route to India. He said, 'I believe that the earth is round and that by sailing westward, I shall find a shorter route.' He pleaded for money and promised that his discovery would make Spain rich and powerful. But neither King Ferdinand nor Queen Isabella believed him. They were afraid to entrust him with the money necessary for the voyage. Besides, Columbus wanted to share some of the profits, too. The king and queen and their advisers thought he was asking too much, so they refused to help him."

De Torres' face darkened as he continued: "De Santangel stood there in the palace listening very attentively. His heart ached for his fellow Jews who would have to leave Spain, their beloved home. Suddenly a thought struck Luis de Santangel, 'Perhaps if I offer my help to Columbus, India will become a refuge for our people.' So De Santangel turned to the king and queen and said, 'I will supply the money. I should love to see Spain grow ever wealthier.' "

"Let us hope for a successful voyage," the Marranos around him called out in chorus.

"Yes, for the sake of Spain and our Jewish brethren."

De Torres, his face flushed with hope and his eyes shining very brightly, got up and leaned over the rail. At that moment he saw a sailor run towards them excitedly.

The sailor looked to the right and to the left and all around. He had something important to tell.

De Torres, impatient, called out, "Hurry, hurry, what is it?"

The sailor whispered, "The sailors are planning mutiny!"

"What? Mutiny? After we have gone through all this trouble! And after we are so far out!" Alfonso Caballeria exclaimed angrily. "What's their plan, anyway?"

The sailor hesitated. Again he began to look around.

"Do tell us all you know. Maybe we can stop them," Sanchez urged.

The sailor wiped his perspiration and continued:

"They said they would throw Columbus overboard and then return to Spain."

Everybody got excited and worried. "How will they explain his death to Ferdinand and Isabella?" Sanchez continued.

But this news was too much for De Torres. The hope with which he tried to encourage the people and himself left him. He grew pale and dropped to the floor.

Everyone's attention was on the sailor as he continued to say:

"But they are afraid of the sea-monsters. And I don't think . . ." The sailor suddenly pointed to De Torres.

"Look! Look!" he cried. "De Torres! De Torres!"

"Where's the ship's doctor? The doctor! Dr. Bernal! Dr. Bernal," everyone was calling.

In a moment the doctor was at the side of De Torres. Calmly Maestro Bernal drew back De Torres' eyelids and his lips. Then he said softly to the startled group, "He will be all right in a few minutes. He has only fainted."

He forced some medicine between the lips of De Torres.

"Yes," said De Torres, opening his eyes and speaking as if nothing had happened, "we will find a refuge for our fellow Jews."

And the ship sailed on.

Land at Last!

Now the ships had reached the open sea. The rough waves tossed them so high that the crew expected the ship to capsize at any moment. Yet they sang on; only now, though the melody was the same, it sounded like a funeral march. It was clear that they were singing only to keep up their spirits.

> We will reach the East
> Though we are westward bound.
> West will bring you East
> Because the earth is round.

> That the earth is round
> You surely all must know
> For from his travels wide
> Columbus taught us so.

Suddenly something strange appeared! A sea full of grass—a sea of grass! Suppose they become entangled in those weeds!

13

Someone on the boat Nina cried, "Let us turn back! We don't want to die! Let us return before we are swallowed up by monsters!"

On the Pinta someone cried, "Let us drown this man Columbus and be free men again."

A third sailor shouted, "Look at those falling stars! We must turn back!"

Columbus and De Torres tried to calm the crew by explaining that the falling stars which so terrified them were good signs from heaven.

Week after week passed and still they sailed on. Then, when they had almost given up hope they noticed birds flying above them. Those were unmistakable signs of land. At sunset the crew on the Pinta climbed up the masts in order to be able to see better.

Someone asked, "Who will be the first to go ashore? Who gets the honor of having discovered this new route?" Excitement grew. Everybody talked at once. Before they realized it, they had returned to the discussion of the first day. The voice of Marco, the surgeon, rang out, "Do you know that even Columbus is a Jew? But at the court, in order to get a hearing, he had to say he was a Catholic, for no one would have listened to a Jew."

"Oh, pshaw," said De Torres, "that is just talk. No one really knows about that. However, . . ."

"It seems ridiculous to worry about honors," the captain of

the Pinta grumbled, "when, as a matter of fact, we shall all go down in the sea, completely forgotten."

A few days later, one of the sailors cried: "I see it! There it is again! Yes, it's most certainly the branch of a tree. Its leaves are still green, and land cannot be far off!"

That night no one slept. At two o'clock one of the crew cried, "Land, land! I see the reflection of the moon on the sand." "Land, land!" the glad cry rang out but not until dawn could they really be sure.

When the sun rose they saw that they had actually reached land. They rushed to the task of dropping anchor. At last the ships were safely moored. Columbus, Luis de Torres and a few others went ashore. They planted the Spanish flag of green on the shore. Upon it appeared the initials "F" and "I," for Ferdinand and Isabella. Then they knelt to pray. They were tired and oh, so glad to be on land again.

"These magnificent trees, heavy-laden with fruit, these beautiful flowers, and this lovely island must be a new part of India. We shall call it 'San Salvador,'" Columbus said.

Little did they dream that they had landed on the shores of America. Columbus turned to Luis de Torres and said, "Since you can speak Chaldaic, Arabic and Hebrew in addition to Spanish, you shall be the first man to go inland. Perhaps the natives will understand you."

All were surprised that the honor of being the first to go inland would go to a Marrano—a Jew. This was 200 years be-

fore the Pilgrims landed in America. And it was Luis de Torres
—a Jew, who was the first to look over the land.

The crew remained behind while Luis de Torres went
ashore. But when, after two days, he had not returned they became restless. Some said they would go out and search the land
for themselves. They said they were not afraid, and would need
no leader. But Columbus and Dr. Bernal held them back. They
pointed out that the men knew nothing about the natives, and
that it would surely be better to await De Torres' return.

The third day passed. The crew was becoming more
alarmed. But when, on the fourth day, Luis de Torres had still
not returned, even Dr. Bernal and Columbus began to fear
for him. Perhaps he had been killed by some of the natives!
Should they go in search of him? They decided to be patient.

Toward sunset of the fourth day, when they had about given
up, De Torres appeared. Why had he stayed so long? What kind
of people lived on the land? Was this very different from any
other part of Asia? They asked him so many questions that he
scarcely knew how to begin.

Then he said, "On this land I found people very different
from the Indians I have seen before. They have copper skin and
long black hair. They sit on the ground and hold fire in their
hands. They go about naked, their bodies painted with many
colors. They light one end of something that looks like dry
leaves—it's called tobacco.

"These men seemed peaceful enough. They came over and

stroked my hands and face. They said in sign language that they had never before seen a man with white skin. Then they brought cotton and ornaments and live parrots to trade. They showed me colored glass which they seem to value highly. They are ready to give a live parrot for a small piece of colored glass.

"And I saw a strange bird, such as we have never seen. It looks like a peacock. I called it, in Hebrew, 'Tukki' (De Torres was speaking about the turkey). This is a beautiful land. I should like to make it my home." Then they all burst into song:

> Though we were westward bound,
> The East at last we've found,
> Since this land we've really reached
> The earth is surely round.

Some fairly danced with joy. They had set out with little hope, uncertain what might happen to them, and now here they were, about to take possession of a desirable land. It was Luis de Torres, a Jew, a Marrano, who had been the first to set foot on American soil, to discover tobacco and the turkey.

In all the hubbub, no one thought of Rodrigo Sanchez as he stood there trembling with joy; his lips moved:

"Our efforts have not been in vain," he was murmuring. "Now it will be easy to come to India. Our people will at last have a refuge."

None of them knew that they had found a new country. Sanchez did not know how truly he had spoken.

Never Give Up

Turkey is possible—
But who can go?
Spain and Portugal—
No—no—no.
To Holland then,
Let us flee
To Holland we shall go.

ONE cold wintry night—a few years after Manoel had settled in Amsterdam he took his son Menasseh on his knee and said: "Today, Menasseh, I shall tell you a true story—not a made-up one." Menasseh was very glad, because he always liked true stories best. His father began:

"You know, Menasseh, before you were born I lived in Spain and in Portugal. There I was a Marrano, that is a man who was secretly a Jew but who made believe he was a Christian. One day I was caught reading our holy Torah in an underground synagogue. Spanish officials found out that at heart I was really a good Jew so they threw me into prison where I was tortured until I thought I should die.

"Weeks passed. Then, one day, two guards entered the prison and called out all the Marranos. They put yellow mitres * on our heads and sanbenitos † over our garments. Then we were all ordered to leave our dungeon. What was in store for us now, we wondered.

"We were led into the market place. Though the sun had not yet risen, the market place was crowded. Men and women, boys and girls, old and young—all were there. Some were learned men, some were business men and others, soldiers. There were men selling peanuts and balloons. There were magicians who could swallow swords. And all of them were waiting for the great event, the *auto-da-fe* (as it was called). Then the ceremony began. This is what happened.

"A monk dressed in black held up a huge cross. This was a sign that all singing and merry-making must stop. Behind the monk followed the bishops dressed in gold, purple and white. They walked under a canopy carried by boys dressed in white and scarlet. Then followed various church officials, dressed in brilliant colors, and carrying colorful banners. After them came the three Inquisitors dressed in black. They looked cold and merciless, like men of iron. Just the sight of them made one's

* A tall head-dress ending in two points, worn by church officials.
† Sanbenito—a loose, yellow garment worn by convicts of the inquisition.

blood run cold. Behind them, we, the Marranos, marched, carrying lighted tapers.

"When the procession had reached the platform upon which sat many important people, we stopped. Each one of us was ordered to step up on a little platform, under which lay dry wood, ready to be kindled. At a sign from the Inquisitor the fires were lit and soon the flames crackled. Some of us grew faint at the sight of the rising flames. Others stood up courageously and with their last breath prayed 'Shema Yisroel Adonoy Elohenu, Adonoy Echod! Hear O Israel, the Lord our God, the Lord is One!'

"The burning of these human beings was called the *auto-da-fe*. The Spanish Catholics thought that by burning people who did not worship as they did, they would save them from burning forever in hell.

"Though I, too, had mounted a platform, the wood under it had not yet been lit. A monk came over to me and explained, 'You see,' he said, 'we discovered that you were innocent and should not have been accused. In the meantime, however, all your possessions have been taken from you and there is no way for you to get them back.'

"Exhausted with fear and the grief of seeing my friends die in the flames, I returned home. I decided to leave Spain forever. I resolved that my child should not be forced to lead the sort of shameful life I had led. I would use every penny I had to take my family to Holland, for it was the only country besides Turkey that was opening its gates to the Jews. That's how we came to live in Holland."

Menasseh sat gazing at his father. Then he said: "Father, when I grow up I shall not let such things happen to the Jews."

That little Menasseh became the great Rabbi Menasseh ben Israel of Holland. His congregation prayed and studied in a synagogue which had been built by the Dutch Jews three hundred years before Menasseh was born.

One Sabbath morning Menasseh said to his people, "The Jews are still suffering in Spain and Portugal. And now they are being driven from Poland, too. We must find a new home—a place of refuge for our people. Where shall they go?

"Our prophets said, 'Behold, I will bring them from the North country, and gather them from the ends of the earth, for I will comfort them, and make them rejoice from their sorrow.'

"Now, as the prophets foresaw, we have been scattered to nearly every part of the world; but there are scarcely any Jews in England. If we settle there we shall then have fulfilled our mission. Throughout the world we shall have taught that God is One, and all of us are His children. Then our wanderings and our suffering will cease. Peace will come to earth. Messiah, the saviour, will come."

"That's easier said than done," someone whispered.

"England won't admit the Jews," grumbled another.

But they listened respectfully as Rabbi Menasseh continued:

"I believe that if England accepts the Jews, both England and the Jews will benefit." Then, with glowing eyes he cried: "I pledge myself, my whole life, to help the Jews find a home in England."

The sermon was over. Yet no one moved. The people were thinking about what the rabbi had said. The more they thought about it the more hopeful they became. "Of course," one said to another, "once the rabbi explains to the Gentiles how important it is for the Jews to be admitted to England, all the Gentiles will help, because they love Rabbi Menasseh."

And the rabbi set to work. He wrote letter after letter to influential Englishmen, and at last received an invitation from Richard Cromwell, the Lord Protector, to come to England.

* * *

Leaving for England! Rabbi Menasseh ben Israel was leaving for England! He who had lived, worked, and studied all his life in Amsterdam would leave his home, his family and friends and go to England. Even now, when trains and aeroplanes carry you so quickly that you can soon return, it is no easy thing to leave your family. You can imagine how much harder it was at the time of Menasseh. But Menasseh had a great mission, and nothing would keep him from reaching his goal.

The road is tiring,
The way is long,

But a mighty aim
Will keep him strong.

*   *   *

It was a balmy day in September when Menasseh arrived in England. Not only the Jews of Spain nor of Holland, but the Jews of the whole world had sent Menasseh to England to plead that they might be allowed to enter that country. Would that plea be granted? Many were the hearts that beat impatiently! Many were the hopes that went along with Menasseh.

When Menasseh arrived in England he went to live in the part of London known as the *Strand*. From this place he could easily reach the group of Marranos who had settled in the city, and also the officials at Whitehall, as the City Hall of London was called.

In Menasseh's luggage the most important article was a bundle of letters to Cromwell, the real ruler of England.

As I have told you, Menasseh came to England in September. You know the holidays of Rosh Hashono and Yom Kippur occur in that month. For the first time in 365 years these holidays were being properly observed in England. The Jews attended the synagogue, read the prayers, blew the shofar, sang Kol Nidre and fasted on Yom Kippur.

But Menasseh did not forget his purpose. The holidays over, he dressed in his best clothes. He put on his short velvet coat and his wide Dutch cap, which looked almost like an umbrella.

Menasseh who was short and stout might have looked funny in this costume; but his grey hair and clear blue eyes gave him a distinguished and lovable look.

It all seemed like a dream. He, Menasseh, a Jew, was going to Whitehall, the English City Hall. He, Menasseh, would set the terms upon which the Jews would enter. Menasseh went over those terms in his mind:

1. The Jews must be protected against any hurt.
2. They must be allowed to build their own synagogues and worship in them as they please.
3. They must have their own places of burial.
4. They must be allowed to trade freely.
5. They must be allowed to have their quarrels settled by their own rabbi.
6. All laws which had been made against the Jews should be removed.
7. In return for these rights, the Jews when admitted must take the oath of allegiance to England.

With his papers under his arm, Menasseh was approaching Whitehall.

*   *   *

On the Outside . . . With him went the hopes of the whole Jewish people. How would he be received? Would Menasseh be allowed to read the petition? His heart was pounding so that he stopped before the door to take a deep breath. At last he was there in Whitehall. With trembling hands he handed the clerk his letter—his petition to Cromwell. The clerk took the paper and walked into the Council chamber. Menasseh stood tense, waiting for the reply. Perspiration trickled down his forehead.

Within, the assembly had just been called to order when the clerk presented Menasseh's petition. Cromwell, frowning at the interruption asked: "Gentlemen, what is your pleasure? Shall we allow this respected Jew to enter, or do you think we may express ourselves more freely if he is not here?" They decided not to admit Menasseh.

After a few minutes which dragged like hours, the clerk returned. "I am sorry," he said politely, "Mr. Cromwell will read your petition, but you will not be allowed to enter."

"Does this mean failure?" Menasseh wondered. Was this to be the end of his great adventure? Menasseh was not discouraged. His mission was too important. "They do not understand us," he reflected. "That is our greatest difficulty."

He returned to his house and that very day began work on a book. When it was finished he called it by two Latin words, *Vindiciae Judaeorum* which means, in defense of the Jews. It turned out to be his most important work, and it became so famous that it was translated into German, French, Italian and Polish. In this book Menasseh told the Christians how false was the idea that Jews had ever used blood—Christian or any other kind—in their holiday celebrations. Menasseh showed that the Jews were fair and honest in their business dealings. He ended

TODROS
GELLER

the book by saying, "If I lie, then may all the curses mentioned in the Bible come upon me and may I never see the return of the Jews to the Holy Land."

*   *   *

Inside Whitehall . . . What was happening in Whitehall? Cromwell took up Menasseh's petition and read its terms. Then, looking up with a twinkle in his eye, he said:

"In my opinion these Jews ought to be admitted. They will help our trade. They will bring it over from Holland, Spain and Portugal. Furthermore, if we have them here with us—then we can hope some day to persuade them to become Christians."

The Council did not agree with Cromwell. The Jews were asking too much. The Council would admit the Jews to England, but not on the terms stated. Cromwell was a sharp and clever man. So he turned to the assembly and said: "It is clear. I shall have to make my own decision. Pray that I may act wisely."

So ended the meeting on which Menasseh had staked all his hopes. The question was never again officially considered.

Cromwell decided it was best to allow the Jews to come in, not officially, but privately, singly, whenever they pleased. Cromwell assured Menasseh that those Jews who would come, would be protected. Can you imagine Menasseh's disappointment when he heard that? He wanted the Jews to go there in large numbers, not just a few at a time.

Still Menasseh stayed on in England. He continued to work on the book which later became so famous. He still tried to influence Cromwell and his Council. But Menasseh's son, who had come with him to England, died. Then nothing—the learned discussions, the conversations, the petitions—none of it seemed important. Menasseh, sick and disappointed, returned to Holland with his son's body.

But what had happened in England? Had Menasseh's work been wasted? Weren't the Jews coming into England?

The Jews were coming into England, a few at a time. There were no laws against their coming, so the English did not refuse to admit them. Thus, indirectly, Menasseh's hope was realized.

Though this happened many years after Menasseh's death, it was because of his efforts that the Jews did come to England. Though the Messiah did not come, yet it was for the good of England, the Jews, and the whole world, that the Jews were permitted to live in that country.

On the Wings of a Dragon

Sleep and rest, sleep and rest,*
Messiah will come to us soon.
Rest, rest on mother's breast,
Messiah will come to us soon.
Messiah will come to this world at last,
Then all our sorrows and woes will be past.
To us and the world a boon,
Soon, in our day, oh soon!

"He is coming! He is coming! Clear the way! Spread the carpets! Sabbatai Zevi, the true Messiah is coming to take his daily bath in the sea!"

"In the sea? But this is the middle of December!"

"Yes, Zevi can do it, because he is the Messiah. He does not feel the cold, and it does not make him sick."

* To be sung to the tune of Tennyson's "Sweet and Low."

Zevi, tall, dark and handsome, his eyes raised heavenward, walks along holding a silver fan in his hand. He does not walk on the carpets spread for him. At times he touches someone with his silver fan. And how great is the joy of one so touched! He has become a different man. Now he has become a holy man, for the Messiah has made him holy by his touch.

Zevi walks on. Throngs follow him as he sings in a beautiful rich voice. His kindly eyes seem to call men, women and children to him.

Yes, this is a cold winter night, but everybody is out, following Zevi to the sea, to the sea for his daily bath. Winter and summer, night and day, Zevi must have his bath in the sea.

And what has given this handsome youth such strange notions?

Even as a child Zevi was different from all the other children. He never joined them in their play. Instead, he would wander off to the woods, alone. There Zevi would sit by himself for hours, listening to the birds and insects and singing the songs his mother had taught him. One of them he liked better than all the others——

> Sleep and rest, sleep and rest,
> Messiah will come to us soon.
> Rest, rest on mother's breast,
> Messiah will come to us soon.
> Messiah will come to this world at last,

Then all our sorrows and woes will be past.
To us and the world a boon,
Soon, in our day, oh soon!

Zevi tried to study the Talmud but he did not like it. He was much happier when he studied the Kabbalah, that collection of interesting writings filled with fanciful and imaginative stories. From those stories he figured out that in the year 1648 the long-hoped-for Messiah would come. Then all wars would cease and all troubles would vanish from the earth. All people would be kind to one another and the whole world would be happy.

One day, as Zevi was sitting in the woods all alone, with only the twitter of the birds and the buzzing of the insects about him, he sang his mother's song. The thought came to him:

"Suppose I were that hoped-for Messiah! Suppose I *am* the Messiah who was sent down to save the Jewish people—to redeem them from all their suffering."

Zevi liked to put thoughts into rhyme. He snatched a pencil from his pocket and began to write hastily: "Let's see," he said, "Messiah—Messiahs——"

Messiahs, Messiahs
Many wish to be,
But before all others
Comes Sabbatai Zevi.

Not such good poetry. He would try another stanza! Yet it really said the thing he wanted to say. He reread his rhyme:

> Messiahs, Messiahs
> Many wish to be
> But before all others
> Comes Sabbatai Zevi.

Zevi suddenly arose and ran home to read his Kabbalah, to read the books full of exciting stories. Such strange riddles and secrets! Zevi thought: "From my study of Kabbalah I have figured out that in the year 1648 the Messiah will come. This is the year 1648. All that I have to do now, to prove that I am the Messiah, is to act out the stories in the Kabbalah."

Now there was a general belief that no one but the Messiah would dare to utter in full the Lord's name, *Jehovah*. So Zevi ran into the synagogue and, right in the midst of the prayers, called in a loud, shrill voice: "Je-ho-vah, Je-ho-vah, Je-ho-vah." Some of the pious Jews nearly fell off their benches, they were so frightened; others fainted. There was a turmoil. Zevi had dared utter the Lord's name! Was then Sabbatai Zevi the Messiah? Should they prepare to gather up their belongings for all to share equally? Were they all to go back to the Holy Land, under Zevi's leadership? Had the long-looked for Messiah come at last?

Zevi, a young man of only twenty-two! Was he going to upset the whole world? No, no, Zevi, not so quickly! The rabbis,

shocked by his actions, would not allow it. And so Zevi was driven out of Smyrna, the city in Turkey where he was born. With him went many of the men who believed in him.

*   *   *

Do you suppose that being driven from his home cured Zevi? Of course not. It only helped to remove whatever doubts he still had. Now he was really beginning to believe himself the Messiah. For this was just as it had been written in the Zohar, one of the great books of the Kabbalah. The Messiah was to suffer, and suffer much, before he could redeem his people.

During his travels, Zevi had been married twice, and each time divorced. And then one day he had a new idea. He announced that he was again to be married, and invited all his followers to the ceremony. Of course they were excited. Whom would Zevi marry now?

When the guests arrived, Zevi arose and holding aloft a Torah, embroidered in gold and purple, he said, solemnly, "My people, I am about to be married, not to a woman, but to the Torah, the *Daughter of Heaven,* because I am the Messiah, the *Son of Heaven.*"

With the Torah in his arms, he stepped under the bridal canopy and, placing a ring on the scroll, he said, "Behold, thou art wedded to me according to the law of Moses and of Israel."

This time the rabbis of Salonica, where the scene took place, became greatly alarmed about Zevi, and they too drove him out.

The would-be Messiah travelled from one city to another until he reached Jerusalem, where good luck was awaiting him. Here as elsewhere, the Jews had suffered so much that they were ready to believe in miracles. Here, too, they remembered the song of the Messiah——

> Sleep and rest, sleep and rest,
> Messiah will come to us soon.
> Rest, rest on mother's breast,
> Messiah will come to us soon.
> Messiah will come to this world at last,
> Then all our sorrows and woes will be past.
> To us and the world a boon
> Soon, in our day, oh soon!

Anyone courageous enough to proclaim himself the Messiah, would be accepted and followed. What would Sabbatai Zevi do now?

Sabbatai was much older and wiser now. He knew much better how to make people believe things he wanted them to believe. He remembered that, according to the rules of the Kabbalah, the Messiah was to go without food, suffer the severest cold, and torture his body in many ways. All of this, Sabbatai began to do. He would take icy baths in the sea. He would stay up all night singing Psalms in his beautiful voice. Then he would go to the graves of the pious and pray. Zevi explained that, in this way, he would bring the spirit of the holy men to himself. As he prayed, he wept so much that his followers said he shed buckets of tears. In all of this, Zevi was doing what he had read about in the Zohar.

But Zevi had a lively imagination and he thought up many new things. When he walked through the streets he sang and threw candy to the children and stopped to caress them. In this way the mothers too became interested in Sabbatai.

Now for Zevi's lucky turn. The Jews of Jerusalem were being taxed very heavily. It was indeed impossible for them to pay their taxes. And the punishment for not paying taxes was death. How then were the Jews to save themselves? Zevi had the answer.

In Cairo, Zevi had met a kind Jew who was very rich. This Jew had enough money to pay the taxes for years to come. All that had to be done was to send a messenger to him. And who should that messenger be? None other than Zevi, himself. Trembling with excitement, Zevi offered to go to Cairo. To himself he said: "I will save the Jews from death! Then it will be easy for me to proclaim myself the savior, the redeemer of all Israel —the Messiah." Zevi chuckled as he thought of the lines he had written about the Messiah in his childhood:

"Messiahs, Messiahs—many wish to be
But before all others comes Sabbatai Zevi."

What a journey, what a mission! Zevi must advertise it, so the whole world should know about it. First of all, Zevi had a special ship built on which only Hebrew was spoken. The sails, made of silk, had Hebrew letters on them. When everything was ship-shape Zevi set sail. But a storm came along and tossed the ship hither and thither. It looked as though Zevi and his hopes would go down in the sea. Zevi, however, took out his mantle and, waving it back and forth while reciting some strange words, stopped the storm. That was the story told by his followers. But historians say that Zevi left the ship and traveled safely on land to Cairo. And there we shall leave him while we see how, in Poland too, something was happening to help Zevi.

* * *

The day was cloudy. In the city, the air was cold and dreary enough—but in the cemetery near-by, things looked even gloomier. A Jewish family had come to the cemetery to visit a grave. Suddenly they heard weeping. Then to their great surprise they saw a beautiful young girl sitting on one of the tombstones, sobbing.

"Why are you crying?" asked one of the women kindly.

"Last night," said the girl, "my father's ghost came and carried me out of my bed, to this cemetery."

The group gathered about her, amazed. The girl continued, "Do you see that convent up there? That's where I live. That's where I was brought up. They tried to make me forget I was a Jewess. They tried to make me forget my mother and father.

But they could never do that!" Then, with a wild look in her eyes, she cried, "I'll never forget how those Cossacks came and massacred our family, how they killed my father and mother; how they drove my brother away. Everyone fled, forgetting me, a little girl of six. The nuns found me and brought me to the convent. They cared for me and brought me up like a Christian nun. But I am not a nun. I don't want to be a nun. I am going to be married, and not to an ordinary man, either. I was born to be the bride of the Messiah, the Redeemer of Israel." As the girl spoke her eyes lit up as with some inner fire. She was beautiful.

These kindly Jewish people took the girl along with them. Later they found her brother in Amsterdam and sent her to him. From there this girl, who called herself Sarah, went to Leghorn, Italy. While she was in Leghorn, Zevi heard of her. Nothing more fortunate could have happened to him. He immediately sent Sarah money to come to Cairo and, in the home of the kind, rich man (Raphael Joseph Chelebi), Sabbatai was married to Sarah, the Polish Jewess. The rich man gave all his wealth to Zevi, who returned in triumph to Jerusalem. And just as Zevi had planned, his fame spread far and wide.

The Turkish Jews began to think of Zevi and not the Sultan, as their ruler. They sent him whatever money they had. Rumors said that he was going to overthrow the government. Zevi was becoming a real danger. The Sultan, afraid of what might happen, ordered Zevi to appear before him. This meant another

journey and another show, for he was in high spirits. Again
Zevi sang his mother's song:

> Sleep and rest, sleep and rest,
> Messiah will come to us soon.
> Rest, rest on mother's breast,
> Messiah will come to us soon.
> Messiah will come to this world at last,
> Then all our sorrows and woes will be past.
> To us and the world a boon,
> Soon, in our day, oh soon!

In spite of his excitement Zevi arranged his affairs very carefully. He divided the world among 26 of his most faithful followers. They were the princes of his lands, and he was the king
over all of them. Then he started on the journey.

Again the weather was stormy, and the journey took weeks
longer than it should have taken. This gave Zevi's followers
another chance to invent miracle stories about him. They told
how storm and wave obeyed the Messiah. As a matter of fact,
Zevi and the crew had to make a forced landing and Sabbatai
was arrested by Turkish officers. What a fall for Zevi! He, the
would-be Messiah, was put in chains, brought to Constantinople
and thrown into prison. Though Zevi was astonished, he asked
no questions. This was another of the sufferings of the Messiah.

When news of his capture spread, thousands of Zevi's followers came to visit him in prison. From every country they

came—Jews from Jerusalem, with striped cotton gowns and soft felt hats; Polish Jews, with fox skin caps and long caftans; "German, Russian and Spanish Jews; Syrian Jewesses, with long black eyelashes; Egyptian Jewesses, with sweeping robes and black head-shawls; Jewesses from Tunis, clad in the gold and silver trousers that the Turkish women wore." They brought him gifts, all they could carry, for they believed that he would be their redeemer. They would have given even their lives for him.

The followers of Sabbatai Zevi believed he would soon lead them into the Promised Land. All work came to an end. Buying and selling stopped. They printed his name, with all sorts of artistic trimmings, in the synagogues. They offered up special prayers for him. They fasted for days at a time, and rolled naked, in the snow. This was to cleanse them of their sins, so that they might enter the Kingdom to Come. They tried to do everything that had ever been mentioned in the tales that had grown up about Sabbatai Zevi, who was to be their Messiah.

Suddenly, one day a messenger from the Sultan elbowed his way through the hundreds of Zevi's followers who stood outside the prison. Before anyone could realize what was happening, the messenger reappeared with Zevi riding on a camel before him. The whole struggling, excited mass of disciples followed. Presently the King's messenger and the prisoner vanished into the palace of the Sultan. The guards halted the crowd at the gates. What would happen to their Messiah now? They would remain outside and await the news.

Meanwhile, Zevi, dazed, found himself standing before the Sultan. He heard a voice saying, "Sabbatai Zevi, the time has come for you to give up this pretense. You are no Messiah. You are a traitor. Your life hangs in the balance. Accept the religion of Mohammed, the true prophet, or you die!" Zevi's head was aching. He stared wide-eyed at the Sultan.

While this was going on within the palace, the mob outside was raging: "What is happening to Sabbatai Zevi, our Messiah? We will enter the palace and see with our own eyes. Yes, we will see Sabbatai Zevi with our own eyes!"

To quiet the throng, the sentries permitted a few of the people to enter the palace. They saw an attendant place upon Zevi's head a white Turkish turban, and about his shoulders a green mantle. They heard the Sultan say to Zevi, "You will wear these as a sign that you have accepted the religion of the Mohammedans. You shall then become my doorkeeper."

When his followers heard these words, they cried: "What a shameful offer for Sabbatai Zevi! Of course he will refuse it! Imagine the Messiah a Mohammedan, the Messiah a gatekeeper; that's impossible! That's an outrage!"

Did Zevi refuse the offer?

Sabbatai Zevi was thinking fast: "If I refuse to become a Mohammedan, I shall be killed. What shall I have gained then? After all, to be the Sultan's gatekeeper is better than to die!"

His followers looked on amazed. With open mouths and staring eyes they saw Zevi throw off his black gown and his

Jewish headdress. They heard a voice say, as if from a great distance, "I am the poor, poor unfortunate Messiah. I have no choice. I must suffer. I am ready."

"Don't do it, Oh, don't do it, Holy Master," some pleaded with tears in their eyes. Others, bitterly disappointed, cried, "For shame, the Messiah a Mohammedan." With flushed cheeks and lowered eyes, they turned to leave the palace. Now that their Messiah had betrayed them, there was nothing left worth living for—nothing but suffering and bitterness. Their Messiah was gone, and all their hopes went with him.

But suddenly one of the followers, with blood-shot eyes, thundered: "Do not give up hope! This is not true—it is not true that Zevi, the Messiah, has accepted Mohammedanism. Hear ye, faithful followers, and I will tell you what has happened." They listened, struck by his words. "Zevi, the Messiah, has been snatched away. On the wings of a dragon he was snatched away! It is not Sabbatai Zevi who made that cowardly decision but an ordinary man, a man of common clay. Our Sabbatai has vanished. I saw it all with my own eyes."

To the faithful followers these words offered great comfort.

"Of course," they began to explain to each other, "the Lord has decided that it is not yet time for the Messiah to come. It is not yet time for Israel to be redeemed, so Zevi, the Messiah has been snatched from the earth. In his place there remains an ordinary human being. It is he who has become a Mohammedan, not our Zevi—not Sabbatai Zevi."

Those poor, miserable, hopeful Jews comforted themselves with this explanation, that at least their Messiah was not a traitor!

But what of Sabbatai Zevi himself? What was he thinking all this time? Zevi was still hoping to play the part of a Messiah. He had a new plan. He persuaded the Sultan to let him speak to the Jews, pretending that he could convert them to the Mohammedan religion.

So clever, tricky Sabbatai Zevi spoke to his followers in this manner: "I am still Sabbatai Zevi, the Messiah. In order that I may bring thousands of Mohammedans to the Jewish religion, I have pretended to accept Mohammedanism. But never fear! I shall not remain a Mohammedan for long!"

Some of his followers believed this. Indeed they too accepted Mohammedanism. They would follow their Messiah in everything. Whatever would happen to their Messiah must also happen to them. But their faith was misplaced.

In spite of Zevi's tricks, luck was clearly against him. His act was over. Not many Jews followed him to Mohammedanism.

Sabbatai Zevi was banished first to Constantinople and finally to a town where no Jews dwelt. There, alone and forsaken, Sabbatai Zevi, the most famous of false Messiahs, died in 1676. Would the Jews ever again place their faith in a false messiah?

Perhaps—for as long as there is suffering, people will continue to comfort themselves with the belief in miracles.

Hail the Duke!

"O Mother! Can you imagine the joy of the Jews in Spain, Portugal and France when they receive your money with which to flee to Turkey and Holland? Your mercy and goodness shall go down in the history of our people," said Reyna Mendes, the daughter of the beautiful, rich Dona Gracia. Dona Gracia lit the Friday night candles, and a peaceful, Sabbath spirit seemed to linger over everything in the room.

"And we, too, shall leave this accursed Venice. I can hardly believe it, I am so happy," cried Reyna as she clapped her hands.

"But hush dear, someone may hear you."

"Yes, someone may hear me," said Reyna bitterly. "How sick I am of being hushed. Always living under cover, always being afraid of my own shadow. But when we get to Turkey we shall be able to live openly as Jews. There we shall celebrate our holidays, and sing our songs. There, where my cousin Joseph Nasi has so much power."

There was a knock on the door. "Sh—sh—quick, blow out the candles and put them into the drawer!" As gracefully as a gazelle Reyna tiptoed across the room, snuffed out the candles and ran to open the door.

"Dona Gracia, your time for making believe is over," a gruff voice said. "You are a Jewess. Therefore you are under arrest, for the law says no Jew may live in Venice."

Dona Gracia stared, wide-eyed. This meant that her money and property would go to the state, while she went to prison. There was no way out.

"And what about my child, my only daughter—what about Reyna?" Dona Gracia cried.

"Oh, this girl? She is the wife of Don Joseph Nasi, is she not? She is to be sent to Constantinople."

"In that case," replied Dona Gracia, relieved, "I am ready. Let us go!" And the beautiful, good, Dona Gracia was taken to prison for being a Jewess.

At the same time, however, Suleiman, the Sultan, received the news through secret channels.

* * *

"Fifty thousand ducats and 30,000 in valuable materials. This is unbelievable, Joseph," said Selim, the Sultan's son, as he beamed at Joseph Nasi, the rich Jew from Venice. "It's only because of you that my father has given this to me. And you were the one to whom he entrusted it. Joseph, my friend, I shall never forget this. You shall become a member of my life-guard (Mutaffarica) immediately. But this is not enough. I would reward you further. Have you any wish?"

"Thank you," replied Joseph. "I ask only this: There may come a Sultan who will not be friendly to Joseph Nasi and his people. So, if it please my master, let him grant my people the city of Tiberias. Let my proud, once rich brothers from Spain, France and Italy have there a home. Then, if ever they are treated cruelly in other lands, Tiberias will be a place of refuge for the Jews."

"Joseph," said the Sultan's son, "it is almost nothing you are asking. That city is so rugged and stony, so filled with wild animals, that I can hardly see of what use it will be to you. You shall have not only Tiberias, but seven islands, besides."

"Thank you again, Selim," replied Nasi, bowing low. "Now I must hasten back to the court where much urgent business awaits me."

"Besides," he added, "I expect news from my Reyna and her mother, Dona Gracia."

Joseph Nasi's power in the court of the Sultan was growing greater; so, too was the jealousy of the French and Italian ambassadors.

Nasi hastened to his court. Though ambassadors from Germany, Poland and the Netherlands awaited him, his first question concerned Reyna and her mother, Dona Gracia. He was so eager that he could hardly control his impatience.

"Haven't they arrived yet?" he asked as he sank back on the low divan which stood on the platform in Turkish fashion. "And is there no word from the French about the 150,000 ducats they owe the Mendes-Nasi family?" Disappointed that there was no word either from Venice or France, Joseph, to control his impatience, turned to other things. He began to discuss his latest plan.

"I have some interesting news," he said to the group of men around him. "When the next boat from Spain arrives with the Spanish Jewish refugees, we shall have some land on which to settle them." The courtiers looked up questioningly. They did not know of any such land. Joseph continued, "Selim has just signed and sealed a paper in which I was given the city of Tiberias and the nearby villages. We shall immediately hire bricklayers, masons, porters and all other laborers to build up the city. Tiberias is barren, rocky and wild. I have even been told that eagles circle overhead and wild goats leap from crag to crag."

"That will not stand in our way. It shall be built up," said Isaac, one of the refugees from Portugal, enthusiastically. Then, thoughtfully, "But how will our people make a living there?"

"That too, shall be taken care of, Isaac. Tiberias is an ideal spot for the growing of mulberry trees. We shall plant them there by the hundreds. Their leaves we shall use to feed thousands of silk worms. We shall buy looms, and learn to weave silk. We shall import wool from Spain and weave fine cloth."

Joseph glowed with happiness at the thought of the future in Tiberias.

Another refugee who held a post of honor in Joseph's court said excitedly, "They will come, our oppressed brothers from Naples, Genoa, and Venice. They will carry the Torah out of Spain and Portugal. We shall establish a Jewish state in Tiberias."

The group stood for a moment, looking far into the distance. They seemed to see their dream come true. Joseph added: "The Mendes-Nasi riches shall increase. We shall use the money to establish this Jewish state."

At the mention of Mendes-Nasi a sudden cloud passed over Joseph's face. In the excitement of planning for the rebuilding of Tiberias he had for the moment forgotten about Dona Gracia and Reyna.

"Have any ships arrived?" he asked suddenly, changing the subject.

"Yes," replied an attendant, "there are ships from Spain, Genoa and Venice. But many of the refugees they carried have been captured by pirates and sold as slaves."

"Here, take this," said Joseph, taking from his pocket a well-filled purse. "Ransom every captive. We shall get back all those refugees."

"Very well, Don Joseph, it shall be done."

At that moment a blare of trumpets announced that guests were entering the courtyard. Joseph arose from the dais and ran down the stairs to meet Reyna, who threw herself upon his neck.

"My own, my beloved," Joseph whispered tremblingly as he embraced Reyna. "Why are you crying and why are you so pale?"

"It's because of Mother," Reyna sobbed. "She isn't here with us. She has been taken prisoner." Reyna gasped for breath through choking tears. "And all our money they took from us, too."

Joseph was speechless with amazement. "Why that sounds like a cruel fairy-tale. It cannot be!" Then, with flashing eyes, he cried: "Who dared do that? Don't they know that Dona Gracia has helped hundreds of refugees? Dona Gracia helped to build synagogues and schools. Surely, a person like that can't be thrown into prison!"

He arose, tall and fearless. The others took courage from him. "We shall lose no time! Selim has now become Sultan. He will help me. Let us go to him at once!"

In the meantime, however, Monseigneur Grandchamp, the most jealous of Joseph's enemies had also laid plans. Monseigneur Grandchamp hated Don Joseph Nasi as did all the Frenchmen. When he heard the news of the Tiberias grant to Joseph, Monseigneur Grandchamp called his courtiers together.

"I have a plan," he said, gleefully rubbing his hands together. "A plan to kill that Jew, Joseph Nasi." His courtiers pricked up their ears.

"Daud, the Jewish physician at the French court, hates the Nasi family. As soon as I learned this, I stirred up his hatred. Then one day he told me he had in his possession letters written by Joseph Nasi to Genoa, Venice, and Florence, containing secrets of the Turkish court in exchange for gold and trade advantages. Furthermore, he has a letter in which Joseph is selling court secrets even to Spain." Grandchamp smiled icily as he said, "Daud is here now. Let us all go to the court and reveal this little secret to Selim."

"Ha, ha," the courtiers laughed hatefully. "That will be something for that clever Jew to work out. Ha, ha," they chuckled, slapping each other on the back.

And they followed Grandchamp to Selim's court.

*　　*　　*

The French delegation was the first to be admitted to the Sultan's court. Just think of it, they had an important court secret! Nasi, the trusted friend of the Sultan, was a traitor!

Selim at first refused to listen to their stories, but the Grand Vizier, who also hated Joseph, persuaded Selim to examine the letters. Mon. Grandchamp had stated the fact and Daud had raised his right hand and was swearing: "So help me, God, these are letters written by Joseph Nasi himself," when Joseph and his courtiers entered.

The Sultan stopped the hearing and asked: "What's wrong, Don Joseph? Speak!"

"O Sultan," Joseph spoke with his usual fearlessness, "we are having difficulties with the French. They refuse to pay the thousands of ducats they owe my family. In addition they have imprisoned Dona Gracia, the mother of my sweetheart."

The Sultan turned to Mon. Grandchamp: "What is your answer to that? Why does your people refuse to pay the debt?"

Mon. Grandchamp had a quick ready reply. "We borrowed money from Christians. These people are Jews—how can it be that we owe them the debt?"

The Sultan understood at once. "You mean that in Spain when these people lent you the money they were Marranos and now they are Jews?" Selim laughed kindly. "That is clever! But the debt shall be paid, with my help. Don Joseph, you shall with my permission, raid any of the French vessels that reach our Turkish ports. And you may demand the release of Dona Gracia in the name of the Turkish government."

At this Mon. Grandchamp and his French delegation scratched their heads. They just kept scratching their heads. They didn't know what else to do.

Selim, the Sultan, pulled himself up in his chair and with a sudden change in tone turned to Joseph again. He narrowed his eyes and pointing to one of the letters given him by Mon. Grandchamp, asked, "Do you recognize this handwriting?" At this point the French delegation stopped scratching their heads. Mon. Grandchamp winked to Daud. (They had not known the Sultan was so clever.)

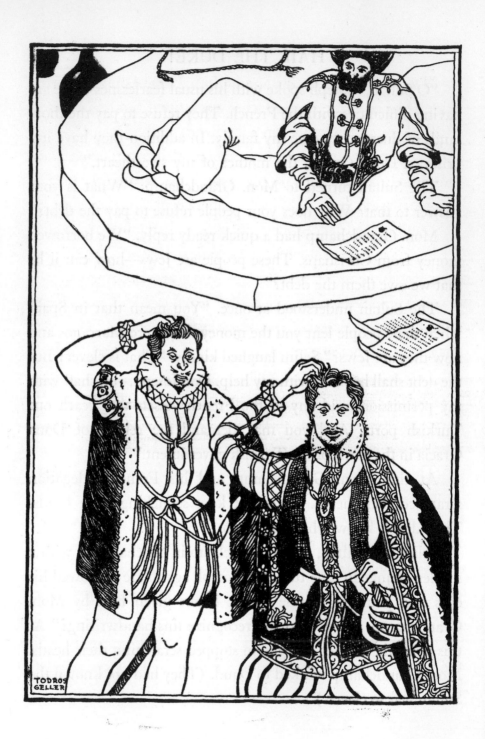

"Do you recognize this handwriting?" the Sultan repeated. Joseph had no chance to read what was written, but he answered, "It looks remarkably like my own hand. Still it is not."

Then in the same haughty manner, Selim turned to Daud and asked, "Can you prove that Joseph has written these? Did you see him do it or do you know anyone who did see him?"

Daud turned pale. His knees began to tremble under him.

"Or," and the Sultan bent even closer toward Daud, "perhaps it is you yourself who have written these documents."

"No! No, I did not write them," Daud cried out as he threw himself at the Sultan's feet, begging for mercy. "No, your majesty, I did not write them."

"Then who did?" the Sultan thundered.

"It was the converted Jewish cook. He gave them to me. He used to work for Joseph, and could copy his handwriting almost exactly. He did it, not I. Please, Sultan, not I."

The forger was sent for immediately. When the Sultan promised to spare his life, he confessed the forgery.

The French were no longer gleeful. They hung their heads when the Sultan said, "Of course Dona Gracia will be taken out of prison. She too, will come to live here in Turkey. And now, dear Joseph, may I have the privilege of giving you a new title, *Duke of Naxos?*"

"Hail! Hail! All hail the Duke of Naxos," rang through the hall. This was too much for the French. They quickly left the court.

Joseph stood up tall and handsome. He tried to express his gratitude. But the courtiers were too noisy and his words were drowned.

"In behalf of my people I thank you. I thank you in behalf of my Jewish brethren," Joseph said happily, though no one heard him.

Troubles Away!

"O Lord, how long! How long, O Lord!" The prayers and tears of the Polish Jews rose to heaven.

And then the Lord said: "The cry of my people is come unto me. Moreover I have seen their oppression." Then turning to the angel who was his secretary, the Lord said: "Gabriel! We must do something for the Jews: Call a meeting of the Heavenly Host, at noon."

"Good, my Lord," answered Gabriel, as he bowed low.

The meeting came to order. "Our problem today," said the Lord, "is to find some great and glorious soul, such as hasn't walked the earth for generations—a soul that will bring light and joy to the suffering Jews."

At this point Satan, who is the bad angel, interrupted: "But there are no man and wife on earth worthy of having such a son." Satan was quite upset. He knew that such a soul would spoil all his evil works.

Just at that moment the gates of heaven were opened. The

heavenly curtains were drawn. The Lord and his angels looked down on a town called Ukop, near Poland. There they saw a man outside the small house of Eliezer. He was crying: "All those who are hungry, all those who are needy, come here. No need for traveling further. Kind Eliezer and his good wife will take care of you." And some distance away another man stood calling, "Eliezer and his wife will take care of the hungry and the needy!"

While the heavenly group watched, Eliezer came to the door with a departing guest and gave him some money.

"That man is worthy of a noble, great-hearted son," one speaker of the Heavenly host said. All agreed except Satan.

"What is great about him?" he argued. "Is he especially learned? Does he study the Talmud night and day? What if he does help a couple of beggars?"

"Granted that he is not a great scholar. But his kind heart outweighs everything," the speaker answered, as if the subject were closed.

"I still say we must give him some more tests," Satan insisted.

"Agreed," said the speaker, "Now whom shall we send down to test Eliezer?"

There was great excitement. Everybody wanted to go. Even Elijah, the prophet, pleaded to be sent.

But the Lord refused, saying, "No, Elijah, you are too kindly and forgiving. You won't give him a fair test. We'd better send Satan, since he thinks there is no one good on earth."

Elijah agreed, and Satan made his plans.

One Saturday afternoon, when there was peace and quiet everywhere, as there should be on the Sabbath, when a pious Jew does no work, carries no loads, nor walks long distances, Satan came down to earth. With staff in hand and knapsack on his shoulders, appearing weary and dusty as if from travel, he entered the house of Eliezer.

Now Satan knew that it would hurt Eliezer to hear from the lips of one who had traveled so far on the Sabbath (which means that he had worked on the Sabbath) the greeting, "Good Shabbos." So, for that very reason, Satan greeted him with a loud and cheery "Good Shabbos." Of course, Eliezer was grieved, but he feared that, by showing it, he would hurt the stranger's feelings. He did not reply, but made his guest comfortable and urged him to spend the night with him.

On Sunday morning when Satan was leaving, Eliezer gave him a goodly sum of money such as he gave to every guest. And not a single word did he mention about his traveling on the Sabbath. For Eliezer was extremely careful not to hurt anybody's feelings.

Satan was greatly troubled. He had hoped to stop the coming of the Great Soul, but he had not succeeded. He threw off his earthly clothes and flew back to heaven. With drooping shoulders and downcast eyes, he had to admit that kind Eliezer deserved to become the father of one who would bring cheer to the dreary lives of the suffering Jews. So Israel of the Great Soul was born!

*   *   *

When Israel was a small boy, his father became very sick and knew he would soon die. He took Israel on his knee and said: "I know you are going to bring joy and happiness and new life to the Jews. You will relieve their suffering." Then he drew Israel a little closer to his breast as he added, "But I shall not live to see it." Eliezer's eyes filled with tears. "Do not forget that the Lord is with you, always. Therefore, fear nothing." And not long afterward, Eliezer died. Israel's mother also died, leaving him alone in the world.

The people of the town had loved Israel's parents, so they took Israel to their homes. They fed and clothed him and even engaged a teacher for him. Israel, however, did not seem to appreciate all that was done for him. Often he did not pay any attention to the teacher. Later, when he was sent to school he often ran away. After a long search they would find him in the woods. There he would sit all alone, listening to the whispering of the leaves and the humming of the bees. Sometimes, amidst rolling thunder or flashing lightning, Israel would sit quietly waiting for the rain to come down.

Since the boy did not seem interested in learning anything, the villagers decided that there was no use trying to get any knowledge into his head. They soon gave up supporting him,

and Israel had to find himself a job. And he did. He became an
assistant to the school teacher. He took the children to and from
school. Even at that time, though Israel was only about nine
years old, the Great Soul within him had begun to awaken. It
seemed to him that he had been chosen especially to take care
of the children, to make them happy. So Israel sang joyful
songs, which he and the children made up together.

I.* O Little birds,
    You're free to fly,
    To fly wher'er you please.
    And we, like you,
    Are carefree too,
    Happy and at ease.

II. Our homes so dark,
    Our teacher sad,
    Are far behind us now.
    God is near,
    The Light is here,
    We have no fear, no fear.

Then one of the older children would sing out:

III. Our leader, Israel,
    Is strong and kind,
    As kind as e'er can be;
    And with him near
    Our troubles drear
    Simply disappear.

IV. He loves the trees,
    He loves the birds
    And all the living things.
    "They're God," he says,
    "They're God," he says;
    And in his soul he sings.

Israel taught the children not to fear their parents and their
teachers but to love them. And above all, he taught the children
never to fear God, but to love Him.

* To be sung to the tune of "Twin Homes" by Sadie Cheifetz, in Goldfarb's
Jewish Songster, No. 1.

When the children sang, they were happy. They forgot their sad, dark homes. They forgot the ugly classroom and the teacher who kept scolding: "Remember and remember," and "Say it over, and say it over again." The children were happy, and their merry songs and laughter made the grown-ups happy too. And a joyous spirit began to spread throughout the world.

Even in heaven the singing of the children was heard. The good angels were glad. But Satan and his bad angels could not bear it.

One day, as the joyous singing filled the air, a wolf suddenly came running toward the children out of the woods. The children were frightened and ran in all directions. Trembling and weeping they ran all the way home and told their parents the story of the big wolf. And the parents decided not to send the children to school with Israel any more.

What a sad day for Israel! What a sad day for the children! But what a glorious day for Satan! He grinned his devilish grin, "Ah," he thought, "now Israel of the Great Soul will not be able to bring joy to the world any more!" But Satan was too hasty.

The children begged to go with Israel, and Israel urged the parents to let them come to school, because he knew he was making them happy. At last the parents consented and Israel and the children marched off again. But the fear of the wolf was still in their hearts. They walked slowly and timidly. Israel, however, remembered his father's words: "God is with you. Fear nothing." Israel began to sing quietly one of the old songs, "O little birds," and one child continued, "You're free to fly," and another added, "To fly wher'ever you please." Then a third and fourth child joined in. Soon they were all singing again,

> "And we, like you,
> Are carefree too."

Once more they were all as merry as ever. Even the big wolf was forgotten and they were again filled with a carefree spirit.

Suddenly a sound—"Aw-oo, aw-oo, aw-oo," came from the thicket. It came closer and louder; and then out jumped the wolf. This time Israel quickly picking up a heavy stone, threw it at the wolf and killed him. None of the children were scared. None ran away. They took their courage from Israel and they all went home together singing:

> "Our leader, Israel,
> Is strong and kind,
> As kind as kind can be.
> And with him near
> Our troubles drear
> Will always disappear."

The next day they found the print of a cloven hoof in the dust near the place where the wolf had been killed.

And the Jews began to feel that there was something unusual about Israel.

* * *

The children grew up and began to study in the Bes Ha-mid-rosh (synagogue) at night. Now Israel thought he could do more for those children by changing his job. And so he became the beadle, or caretaker, of the synagogue. And still no one knew about the Great Heart and Great Soul in Israel. In those days many of the students slept in the synagogue. During the day Israel did not do much. But when the students were asleep Israel would stay awake and study. (There was never a teacher with him; so it must have been an angel who taught him.) When it was time for the students to wake up, Israel would go to sleep, pretending that he had been asleep all night.

One night Zalman, one of the students, tore a page out of a holy book which had been given him by his father. Zalman laid it on Israel's table. When Israel awoke and saw the page he was very happy. Carefully and tenderly he put it away among his books. The next night Zalman again tore another page out of the same book, and placed it on Israel's table. Again Israel took it, and just as he was putting it away Zalman walked over to him and said,

"Now I know that you are a holy man. When my father gave me this book which has come down from Abraham, Our Great Forefather, he said, 'I cannot understand this book. But you go to Ukop and there you will find one by the name of Israel. He is the one who will understand it.' Now here you are and here is the book. Will you be my teacher?"

"Certainly," Israel answered happily, "but you must not

breathe a word about this to anybody. I need many more years in which to study and prepare myself."

Now, just as Israel had sung with the children in order to make them happy, just as he had taught them that God was near them, even within them all the time, so now he taught these grown young men. He would go out to the woods and say:

"How lovely the buzzing insects and the murmuring brooks and green valleys! How glorious it all is! And Israel would begin to dance and clap his hands and, in a sing song tune, chant one of the prayers, "Tov L'hodos," "It is good to give thanks to the Lord . . ."

The students and passersby would be drawn as by magic. They would leave their work, they would leave their books, they would leave the synagogue and run out to join Israel. Before they realized it, they too were dancing, clapping their hands and swaying to and fro. A magic joy seemed to have come over them. Afterward, almost too tired to stand up, they would ask:

"What is it about Israel that makes us want to pray differently? What is there about Israel that warms our hearts and souls?"

"That is just it!" someone would exclaim, "Israel has a great soul and a big heart. Because of his great love of God and men his prayer is as joyful as a song, and as merry as a dance, and he brings new life to everybody!"

"But he is so ignorant! I don't think he can even understand the meaning of the prayers," said one of the youths. This youth had always been taught that anyone who was not a scholar could not amount to much.

"Is he so ignorant?" asked Zalman, a little too flushed and eager. "It may be that he knows more than a good many of us. Perhaps he just doesn't want to show off."

Zalman was going to say more. Then he remembered his promise to Israel and became silent.

"Anyway, what difference does that make? The truth is he has brought joy and life and a new spirit to us Jews," said a pale-looking boy.

"Israel has never sent invitations. He hasn't asked anybody to join him," Zalman continued. "He has never coaxed his students into doing anything."

"That's right," they all had to agree. "It is his way of living, that is, his best way of teaching."

*   *   *

"Ts—ts—ts—what a disgrace!" said Rabbi Gershon to his wife as he shook his head, "My sister, the sister of the great rabbi Gershon, should be married to such an ignorant fellow! You know I tried to teach him something the other day. But I gave it up. He simply will not learn."

"It's all your father's fault," said Rabbi Gershon's wife. "If he hadn't made that marriage contract with Israel, your sister would not have had to marry him. Still, there is something peculiar about it all. Remember the day when he came, on the very date set down in the contract? Remember how you thought it was some beggar at the door?"

"Yes, I remember it all. It still doesn't seem true."

"But it's a good thing they decided to move away from here. I would have given them more than a horse and wagon. Let that ignorant fellow lead his wild life in the Carpathian mountains!"

"But it must be hard work to dig lime in those mountains," said Rabbi Gershon's wife pityingly. "And he does that."

"Yes, and my sister takes it to the city and tries to sell it!" Gershon added as if it were all his wife's fault. "When I think of that, it almost kills me."

But the rabbi's wife, who was more worried about her husband than about his sister said, "What can you do about it? They won't even accept any money from us. That clears us. The best thing to do is to forget about them."

For seven years Israel of the Great Soul lived in the mountains. There, far removed from the hustle and bustle of the city, he was preparing for his great work.

And what was that? To bring joy and hope to mankind!

*   *   *

Whether he was amid the red-gold leaves of autumn or high in the snow-capped mountains, Israel felt himself one with nature, with God and his world.

One day Israel said to his wife, while she was mixing some flour and water for their meal, "I have cured a sick woman with some herbs. I am so happy to be able to do that."

"But how did you do it?" asked his wife with amazement, as she shaped the dough into loaves.

"O, I watched the peasant women and I learned some things about herbs from them."

"*You,* Israel, learnt from the peasant women?" his wife asked teasingly.

"O, I think we can learn from anybody. But, the other day, I cured a woman without any herbs at all."

Israel's wife had the loaves all ready to bake in the sun.

"Oh," she said admiringly, "so it was *you* whom the people in the village meant. They are calling you the *Baal Shem Tov, The Master of the Good Name.*" She carried the loaves out to bake in the sun and quickly returned.

"But how did you do it!" she again asked wholly astonished.

"Why, it's simple, dear. Isn't God the father of all of us? Did you ever see a father who let his son be sick without doing anything for him? Well, if you really and honestly believe that God is the Father of all of us, then you are sure to get better. That woman just trusted in God and she became better."

"But, *I* couldn't have done that for her, Israel. I always knew there was something holy about you," his wife said lovingly.

"And I suppose the other story they told me about you is true, too. They said that once they saw you walking along on one of the high precipices, deep in thought. You came to the edge of the precipice. It seemed you would fall over. Some watched, holding their breath while others screamed out with fear. Then, to their great surprise"—(Israel waved his hand at his wife, as if he didn't believe the whole story.) "But, listen," she pleaded, "listen to what they said happened. The cliff of the other precipice moved up close to fill up the gap, and you walked right on. And you didn't even notice it, I suppose! Israel, you're a miracle worker!"

Then suddenly, with a changed air, she said, "Here is a letter from Gershon. He wants to buy an inn for us. Perhaps we ought to accept this offer! Haven't you learnt enough from the birds and bees? Even they seem to tell you all their secrets. Do let us get out into the world!" she said coaxingly, but still timidly.

And Israel of the Great Soul, Israel Baal Shem Tov, as some called him now, became an innkeeper.

*   *   *

Sauerkraut, pickles, wurst and wine. As you opened the door of the inn, these odors greeted your nostrils.

"You go into your hut, Israel. I'll take care of the business here," his wife said to the Baal Shem Tov.

Though Israel was dressed in peasant clothes like the other men in the room, though he sat at one of the tables and spoke with the simple peasants and innkeepers, still there was something different about him. A kind of light seemed to come from him. Though no one saw it, everyone felt it.

The room was crowded. It served as sitting room, dining room, bed-room, kitchen and bar, combined. It was full of thick smoke. For a chimney there was only a hole in the roof. In order to keep the fire from going out, they closed the hole. Wurst, as well as the clothes, were drying on a line, and a stuffy odor of sauerkraut, pickles and wine filled the room.

It is little wonder that Israel was glad to have his little hut in the forest. Into that little hut he had gathered all his followers from the Carpathian villages. There, for the first time, at the age of 42, Israel began to tell the people that he had come to earth for a special reason—to bring joy and hope to his unhappy people.

*   *   *

Don't fear, little soul,
Don't fear, don't fear.
The Lord is with you,
The Lord is near.

"If you really want to see God you will see Him. No one is as near as God." Thus spoke Israel Baal Shem Tov as he walked along in the open fields near the city of Miedzyboz. Israel now chose to live in this city because it was the most beautiful in the neighborhood. Besides Miedzyboz also had a synagogue 300 years old.

Zalman and others who were following Israel repeated after him "No one is as near as God." Zalman put his forefinger to his forehead and then waved it upwards. As he did this he said, "Aye, aye, aye. If you want to see God you will see him." And all the students did the same thing and repeated the same words, "Aye, aye, aye, if you want to see God you will see Him." It was like the game, "Follow your master." And the students of the Baal Shem certainly loved their master. They all looked up questioningly and waited for the Baal Shem Tov to continue. ("How?" their eyes seemed to ask, though no one said a word.) And Israel did not disappoint them.

"Once there was a very wise, kind king," Israel said. "Many were the people who wanted to get a glimpse of him. But a very long hallway led into the king's palace. Then many rooms had to be passed before one could reach the king. In the hallway and at the entrance to each room there were many valuable treasures. As the people came, they were bewitched by the splendour which was before them. They took the rubies and the diamonds. They forgot about the great king They returned home without ever having gotten any farther than the hallway."

Now Israel's wife had prepared food for Israel and his pupils. But she herself had eaten nothing that day. No one had noticed this, since they were all so interested in Israel's teachings. When Israel seemed to have reached a stopping place, she said, "I'm sorry to interrupt you. I didn't mind going without food myself, but now I have nothing for you and your pupils.

And you won't be able to go on studying and teaching if you don't eat. Now you will have to go to town and get some money from the treasury which the kind people keep for you."

In order not to lose any time, the students went along with Israel. Israel continued to teach them, that is, to tell the story. "But a long-lost son of the king was among the visitors. O, how the son longed to see his beloved father, the king. He was not interested in the rubies and sapphires and diamonds. He just wanted one thing, to see his dear father. The son passed over all the glittering treasures and just walked on and on until he reached the palace and his father, the king. And so it is with God. If only you want to find him, you will surely find him."

By this time they had reached the town. There Israel got some money which the kind people of the city had put away for him. He then stopped at the baker's, bought some bread, and paid him. He stopped at the butcher's and bought some meat. He stopped at the grocer's and bought some groceries. But even then he had not spent all he had.

"Look, I still have some money left," he said to his students. "Let us give that to the poor in the city! And so Israel, without a penny in his pocket, came home, together with all his students. Israel and the students seated themselves about the table and ate their meal. For Israel not only taught his students, but fed and clothed them, and fed even the families of some.

"For the body is as important as the soul," Israel would say. "Each is a part of God.

> For the body must be clean,
> Even as the heart;
> For each and all
> Is of God a part.

By eating and drinking we serve God just as much as by praying. So eat, pray, sing, and be merry. It is only another way of getting closer to God."

And the students rejoiced with the Baal Shem Tov. After they had sung and danced so that even the chairs seemed to jig, Israel continued the topic of the day.

"Once there was a great musician," he said. "This musician played the violin beautifully. As he played, the violin seemed to gain a soul, and a human voice seemed to sing out of it. Those who heard the sweet strains of music were spell-bound. It was so beautiful it did not seem real. They sat as still as statues, listening to every note.

"But along came a deaf man, so deaf he couldn't hear a sound. He began to speak to one of the people. 'Get away, sh-sh,' they pushed him off. The deaf man went on to a second and third person. And suddenly he noticed that all the people were sitting still, without talking, without moving. Because he could not hear the music he could not understand why they all sat so silently. 'Are they all crazy?' he asked.

"Had he not been deaf, he would have understood why they were so still. He would have heard the beautiful strains of the violin. But the blind cannot see and the deaf cannot hear. Only the chosen ones can see and hear. Only the good and the kind can come close to God." Israel had finished the story.

Then his pupils arose and formed a circle about the table. Each put his hands on his neighbor's shoulders and they danced joyfully. Each one knew that the Baal Shem Tov had spoken especially to him. Each one felt that he had come closer to God.

This way of teaching brought Israel many followers. He became the leader of thousands of Jews who called themselves Chassidim. Like their leader Israel, they tried to bring joy and hope and faith to the Jews.

The Fighting Hunchback

A BLUE-GRAY light crept through the windows. Dawn had come. The snow had been falling all night. Icicles were hanging from the roof.

"Süschen," aren't you up yet?" called Mendel as he folded his talis and began to wind up his t'fillin. "Do you know it's almost five o'clock?"

"Oh, yes. Certainly I am up," answered a voice from the bedroom. "But you surely won't take Moishele out on such a day! After all, he isn't even five years old!"

"O, it won't hurt him. He'll grow up strong in our Torah, and that's what we Jews need."

Moses' mother set the teakettle on the fire and began to help Moses dress. She knew there was no use in arguing with his father.

"Here is some nice hot tea and bread. Hurry, Moishele, Father will carry you to school."

77

Meanwhile, Moses' father, in order to lose no time, was copying a few more lines on a scroll, for he was a Sofer, that is, one who copies Torahs on parchment.

Every day, with the exception of the Sabbath, Moses was wrapped in a heavy blanket and carried to school by his father. Moses was a very bright boy and oh, so eager to learn. He soon knew the whole Bible by heart. As they made their way to school Moses' father would say: "Tell me, Moishele, does the Lord want sacrifices of the Jews?" Moses would reply quickly, quoting from the prophet Isaiah, "Lomo li rov zivchechem,— Of what purpose is the multitude of your sacrifices to me . . . wash yourselves, make yourselves clean—do justice."

Now whether little Moses really understood the Bible, we do not know, but we are certain that he *knew* his entire Bible by heart.

For some years, Moses attended the school of the great Rabbi Frankel. One spring day when he was on his way to school, he noticed some children of his own age, who were also on their way. But instead of carrying books, they were carrying baskets of eggs and rolls and muffins, and Moses noticed that they stopped at the houses and sold these wares.

That day at school, Moses could not pay attention as he had always done. He could not forget those poor Jewish boys who lived in the Ghetto just as he did; those little boys who peddled eggs and rolls and muffins.

That night when he came home, Moses did not talk about

all the interesting things he had learned at school, as was his habit. Instead he asked: "Mother, are we too, very poor?"

"Why do you ask that?" said his mother as she looked up in surprise from her sewing.

"Because every day when I go to school I see little poor boys carrying baskets of things to sell. Maybe I ought to do that too! But oh, how I love my Rabbi Frankel and the things he teaches me. And oh, how I should hate to leave my school." Moses began to cry, "but if we're very poor I will do it."

"Don't worry, Moses dear, you won't have to leave your school. Your father and I shall manage."

Moses' eyes began to sparkle again. He jumped up and kissed his mother. "Oh, mother, I'm so happy."

Until Moses was 14 years old he went to the school at Dessau, the city in Germany where he was born. Then, to Moses' great grief, Rabbi Frankel was transferred to Berlin, a city 67 miles away. Crushed in body and spirit, with tears streaming down his face, Moses waved farewell to his beloved rabbi.

Who would teach Moses now? No one in Dessau knew enough to teach him. Would he give up all his studies?

No, no! Not that. Moses knew what he would do. He would go to Berlin. He would seek out Rabbi Frankel and there study with him. So, one early summer morning Moses slipped some clothes into a bag. It was only some underwear, for he had only the suit he was wearing. And off to Berlin Moses went.

Of course, you understand that Moses was not going to ride on a train, nor even in a wagon. His parents had no money for that. He was going to walk the sixty-seven miles all the way from Dessau to Berlin. But Moses didn't mind that. It seemed to him that he could walk to the end of the earth, if only he might continue to study with his beloved rabbi. So on he trudged.

One day, two days, passed. On the third day, Moses began to feel very tired, but he kept up his courage. Berlin couldn't be far away now. Another day passed. He asked a passerby how much farther it was to Berlin. "A long, long way," said the man. The fifth day came and Moses was almost too weary to go on. But all the time he kept his goal before him—Berlin, and Rabbi Frankel. At last, toward evening of the fifth day, he arrived in Berlin at the Rosenthal Gate, the only gate thru which Jews were allowed to pass. He found his way to Rabbi Frankel's school.

Moses was tired and hungry. He looked dirty and shabby. His coat sleeves were worn at the elbows, and his trousers at the knees. What a poor figure indeed! But hopefully Moses went up to the doorkeeper of the school and stammered for admission. (Moses always stammered a little, and now hunger and fatigue made him stammer even more.)

"I have w-w-alked all the w-way from Dessau—t-t-to see Rabbi Frankel"——

"Have you money for your schooling? Are your parents

TODROS
GELLER.

here? With whom will you live? Who will take care of you," the doorkeeper asked.

Moses was bewildered. Had he walked all the way from Dessau only to be turned away? Everything blurred before his eyes. He felt faint, and the floor seemed to rise toward him. But mustering all the voice that he had left he stammered: "I h-have no m-money. But Rabbi Frankel knows m-m-me. I was his p-p-pupil in Dessau."

"Very well, then," said the doorkeeper, swinging open the door.

Moses forgot that he was faint and hungry. He forgot his burning, aching feet. He felt ready to dance a jig. He could think of only one thing, the one thing that mattered. He was in Berlin with his beloved Rabbi Frankel.

*　　*　　*

Many years passed. One day a rich merchant from Hamburg came to see Moses and said: "Our family has been reading your writings, and we admire your beautiful German. We also admire your courage in trying to take the Jews out of the ghetto and make them free. I have a daughter, Fromet, who is eager to meet you. Will you come to see us in Hamburg?"

"Thank you, I shall," Moses nodded modestly.

Moses was short and misshapen, with a hump on his back. Though he had a fine forehead, his eyebrows and cheek-bones were too prominent. Because of his shabby appearance he did

not feel sure of himself. Even among philosophers Moses remained timid and quiet. But he took courage and went to
Hamburg. There he met Fromet Guggenheim. She was not
particularly pretty nor particularly clever, but Moses loved her
at first sight.

They began with the usual polite conversation. Then Moses
said, "I know you're wondering about my hump." Fromet
blushed slightly and looked away. "I think you will be interested
in learning how I happened to have it.

"When I came to Berlin at the age of 14, a rich Jew was good
enough to give me a garret in which to live. This man also gave
me a few meals during the week. All I could afford to buy was
a loaf of bread once a week. On this loaf I marked off enough
for each day. If I had eaten more than just that certain portion
I should have had to go completely hungry for the rest of the
week."

Fromet shivered. Moses wondered, "Is she shuddering, or is
she bored?"

But Fromet cleared away that doubt by exclaiming admiringly, "And while living that way you managed to study
Greek, and Latin, and mathematics and German—and what a
beautiful German you write! And you defeated the great
philosopher Kant in an essay contest and won the prize!"
Fromet added warmly.

"Yes," Moses replied, quietly and modestly. "Those days
were rather difficult, so difficult that they may have had some-

thing to do with the development of this hump. At that time I thought of becoming a rabbi, but I didn't want to give up my writing. I wanted to have time to translate Rabbi Menasseh ben Israel's "Vindiciae Judaeorum" and the Bible. Therefore, I secured a position as a clerk in a silk factory. Mr. Bernhard, the owner, was very kind. He said I had an excellent handwriting and that I was a good mathematician. He made me the book-keeper and soon after that I became a partner in the factory. That gave me time to pore over that wonderful work of Maimonides, *The Guide to the Perplexed.*

At these words Fromet again glanced with embarrassment at the hump on his back.

"Yes," Moses said smiling, "that's why I'm telling you this story because some of my friends say that Maimonides gave me this hump."

"And you do have such wonderful friends!" Fromet glowed. "Some of the greatest Jews and Christians are your friends," she said, with a longing, far-off look in her eyes. She seemed to think, "If I marry this man I shall be hostess to all these great people." But aloud Fromet said, "You have translated the five books of Moses and the Psalms into German. You want the Jews to be able to read German. You want them to be not only intelligent Jews, but also intelligent people. Is that right?"

"Yes," Moses replied. "I want them to become once again a free, educated and cultured people."

"That's all very fine," Fromet blushed as she said, "but why don't you write poetry as you used to do when you were younger? Why don't you work a little for yourself instead of for your people?"

"My dear Fromet, your father and others are mistaken when they think I am losing something by not working for myself. It is much more important that I should show Jews and non-Jews alike that I really love my Jewish people and my religion. I want my people to become better Germans, better men, it is true. But I don't want them to give up their religion. Worrying about that is perhaps another reason why I have this hump," Moses said jokingly. "But the real reason I'll tell you later.

"Why don't you tell me something of yourself? I am not used to talking so much about myself. You may think me very selfish, and then you won't like me."

"Oh, what could I say that would interest you?" Fromet answered shyly. "I haven't written any great books nor thought any great thoughts; nor have I done anything for anybody."

"Well, perhaps then," said Mendelssohn, with a twinkle in his eye, "I shall tell you the real reason for my hump. Then you'll have a chance to do something for someone."

Fromet didn't quite understand, but she said warmly, "Oh do—please do."

"Marriages, as you may know, are made in heaven. Now just as I was about to be born I heard them choosing my wife. To my great sorrow, I learned that the girl who was to be my wife would have a hump. I jumped up quickly and pleaded,

'O, please Lord, don't let that happen. A girl should be beautiful and happy. O, do please give me the hump and let the maiden be beautiful.' "

At this Fromet threw her arms around Mendelssohn's neck, and kissed him; and of course they were married and lived happily ever after, and had six gifted children.

* * *

Soon after their marriage, Lessing, the great German philosopher and poet, came to visit them. Upon entering the house he saw a life-sized china ape in the hallway. Lessing thought it was rather ugly, but he politely said nothing. When he entered the second room he saw three more china apes. In a third room, there were still more.

At last Lessing in a very friendly manner asked: "Moses, why do you choose apes to decorate your home?"

Upon which Moses explained that every Jewish bridegroom was forced to buy a certain amount of china-ware from a new royal china factory. And the buyer had no choice. That was how they happened to have those 20 hideous china apes.

Moses kept them on purpose to acquaint people with some of the ridiculous laws against the Jews. Not only were the Jews kept out of all professions and forced to live in narrow, dirty quarters, but they were also forced to spend their money in such ridiculous ways.

"My dear Gotthold," Moses would say to Lessing, "I will

bring my Jews not to the real but to a new Palestine. My Palestine will be the new European learning."

"That reminds me. What do you think of this little book?"

Before Moses could answer, Henrietta and Abraham, two of Moses' children, ran in breathlessly, crying, "They're throwing stones at us again, and calling us names. 'Jew-boy'—'Jew-girl' they keep calling after us. Is it a disgrace to be a Jew?"

Lessing gave Moses an understanding glance, as he said comfortingly to the children: "That will all be changed after your father has finished writing his books. Those books will help the Jews and Christians to understand one another."

"I wonder," Moses sighed sadly, "whether my books will succeed, if your book, *The Jews,* didn't!"

"The trouble is that most of the Christians do not believe that there are such fine Jews. Now I shall write a play. The hero will be a Jew. That will give them a better idea."

And he did. The play was called: *Nathan the Wise.* And the hero was really Moses Mendelssohn!

When the children had left the room Moses glanced thru the little book which Lessing had brought. "Yes," he said: "I have read this book. It tells all the faults of the Jews and gives reasons for keeping them in the ghetto." As Moses turned the pages, his face flushed with anger and he said: "Every word of this is false, and I shall prove it!"

"By all means, do!" urged Lessing.

The next time Lessing came to visit him, Moses handed him

his booklet, which was an answer to the other. He asked Lessing to read it and give him his opinion of it.

Some time later Moses visited Lessing, who made no mention of the booklet. Another time Moses came, and still Lessing said nothing about it. At last Moses summoned the courage to ask shyly, "Have you read the little manuscript I gave you?"

"Oh, my dear Moses, please excuse me. I have been so busy!"

Moses said nothing. The next time Lessing came to Moses' house he found, as usual, a group of well-known men and women, Jewish and Christian guests. Lessing took out a little book and said, "By the way, Moses, here is another little book about which I should like your opinion."

Moses felt somewhat angry, but in his usual mild manner took the book and assured Lessing he would be glad to read it. How great was his surprise when he opened the packet and found that Lessing had had his manuscript printed, with the title *Philosophical Writings.*

"And here is this little check which the publisher gave me for the copyright," added Lessing.

"My friend, my Christian friend," Moses cried joyfully, "if you and I can be such true friends why can't the rest of your people at least cease persecuting my Jewish brethren? It is clear, I must continue my work in order to make that happen."

"Continue your work, Moses. They will read your writings and they will learn to understand and appreciate your people," his friend replied.

He Never Stops

England . . . "Oh, Monte!" exclaimed Judith Montefiore, her eyes shining with tears of joy, as she looked up at her tall husband. "My dear, you will be Sheriff of London and Middlesex!"

"Yes, Judith dear, I am happy too, but I shall have a lot of difficulty in trying to do my duty. The day I am to take office is Rosh Hashono, the beginning of the New Year. Therefore, I shall have to walk to Westminster instead of riding in my carriage. Then I shall not be able to be present at the inauguration dinner, because it falls on Yom Kippur, which is a fast day."

"Oh, they'll change the date for your sake." And Judith Montefiore was right. The date was changed and Moses attended the inauguration ceremony.

Lord Mayor's day came. Moses Montefiore was to lead a group from the Board of Deputies of the Borough of Ramsgate to bring congratulations to the Queen. On his return Moses told his loving wife, Judith, what had happened.

"When I knelt before the Queen, she touched my left shoulder with the tip of a sword and said: 'Rise, Sir Moses.' Imagine how I felt when I looked up and saw my banner with *Jerusalem* on it floating in the hall."

" 'Rise, Sir Moses' ", she said. Montefiore repeated each word slowly, "and my heart leaped with joy."

*   *   *

Russia . . . "The snatchers, the snatchers! They're coming!" screamed Rachel wildly to her little boy, Sammy. "Go hide, quick! Under the bed—anywhere!"

But Rachel was too late. The snatchers had already seized Sammy. Rachel threw herself sobbing on the bed. The neighbors came running, terrified!

"Like dog-catchers, they come and snatch our children from us!" said one.

"Woe! Woe!" wailed another. "How I hate them! Pfui!" and she spat. "The little ones they steal from us. It is not enough that the law forces the big ones to go! Soldiers they will make of them! Goyim they will make of them!"

"Woe is me! Woe is us! What is to become of us!" cried Leah as she wrung her hands.

"And now the latest decree!" said Joseph as he stood in front of the open fire and warmed his hands. He had just come from the market where he had heard the news.

"It's not enough for them that they don't let us earn our

bread. Now they're throwing us out of our little dwellings."

"It's bad, bad indeed," agreed Lezer, his neighbor. "Whatever little property we have, they will take from us." With deep, sad glances they looked into one another's eyes.

"We who have lived here all our lives! We who have buried our loved ones here, will have to leave this place and become wanderers—'Wandering Jews' forever," groaned another.

There was a brief silence, broken only by the moans of the weeping Rachel. Then Joseph continued bitterly:

"If only we might be allowed to flee to other countries! Then there might be some hope for us. But, no, we may not even do that. We must move fifty miles into the interior of Russia, where they will be able to persecute us even more."

"But the Lord will send us a Messiah," another neighbor continued the conversation. "He will deliver us. Perhaps Moses Montefiore, that *good Jew,* he will deliver us."

The mere thought of Moses Montefiore gave them courage to live on. By now ten men had gathered in the house and Joseph began to intone the afternoon prayer (Mincha).

"Ashre yoshve veisecho." (Happy are they that dwell in Thy House.)

But though they were saying the familiar words of the prayer, those words suddenly had a new meaning. They seemed to say: "Happy are we that we have a Moses Montefiore." And they waited impatiently for the arrival of Moses Montefiore.

* * *

A sleigh was being drawn by trotting horses over a slippery road along-side the densely-wooded, lonely forest. Behind it, running swiftly, so swiftly that they might at almost any minute overtake the panting horses, came the black shapes of wolves, silent as shadows against the gleaming white snow. Bells were ringing, not happily, but in a wild sort of way, to scare off the wolves. Ding-dong, ding-dong, ding-dong, they jangled. The horses kept slipping and sliding, almost falling. Who were the people in this sleigh? Who was brave enough to take such a dangerous journey? It was Moses Montefiore and his wife who were risking their lives for their fellow-Jews in Russia.

At last they arrived at the Palace of the Russian Czar. In their honor the guard for the day was made up of Jewish soldiers. Sir Moses and his wife had arrived on Friday afternoon in time to welcome the Sabbath. The emperor sent two soldiers especially to escort the guests to the services in the Soldiers' Synagogue.

On the following day, Sir Moses arrived at the palace for the interview which had been arranged with Czar Nicholas I of Russia. Moses was led down great halls with highly polished floors. He finally reached the Emperor's room where the brilliance of the crystal candelabras was dazzling. The tall-backed chairs and the velvet hangings were very impressive even to Moses, who had seen many beautiful things in his life. He walked up to the throne and bowed. The emperor, in a friendly way, extended his hand and asked Moses to be seated. Then Moses lost no time in opening the subject.

"Of course," he said, "I've come to see the emperor on behalf of my suffering brethren."

To which the Czar responded, "We are trying to help the Jews by teaching them the Russian language and customs." The Czar spoke as if he did not understand that Moses was talking about the decree.

"I am sure they will not be dull pupils," Moses continued the game for a while. But then he said with determination:

"I know my brethren. I have observed them in different parts of the world. They are honest and loyal subjects. I am certain that Your Excellency will find that the officials of your government agree with me."

His Excellency remained silent. Moses continued: "My brethren in Russia are always ready to fight for their country."

At last His Excellency spoke: "For all you say, they are not flocking to our schools!"

Moses retorted: "Do they have enough clothing on their backs with which to go to school? Do they have enough food? Are they given a chance to earn a living? How then can you expect them to pay for the books and clothing which they must have in order to go to school?"

Sir Moses tried hard to remain calm. But he couldn't help speaking the truth!

Then the Czar spoke with royal dignity: "You may be assured of my sincere desire to improve the condition of the Jews."

"Then Your Excellency will withdraw this bad decree?"

Moses asked hopefully. "The Jews will be allowed to engage in agriculture and handicrafts? For, I repeat, they are very worthy citizens."

"If they are like you," the Czar smiled. "If they are like you," he repeated, "I know they must be worthy." Sir Moses was happy in the thought that the cruel edict against the Jews would be removed.

On his return to England, Queen Victoria made Sir Moses a Baronet of the United Kingdom of Great Britain: "I bestow this honor upon you for your high character, and for your untiring efforts in behalf of your people throughout the world."

"A Baronet, a Baronet," Sir Moses kept saying. He was as happy as a child with a new toy.

"Dear Monte, dear Sir *Baronet* Moses Montefiore," his wife, Judith, exclaimed as she kissed him.

*   *   *

Italy . . . "There, there, little Edgar, don't cry, don't cry. So! I'll wrap you up warmly, and we shall soon be at church," chirped Anna Morisi, the Catholic nurse, as she made funny sounds to amuse little Edgar.

Little Edgar Mortara didn't seem to care whether he was going to Church or any other place. But he did not like to be disturbed in the midst of his nap. Anna, however, had to hurry, for she had only one hour in which to go and return. The Mortaras would be home at four o'clock. She was taking a chance. But she dared it for her religion! And though little Edgar Mortara did not know it, he was baptized and made a Catholic.

The nurse returned home in time. The Mortara's had not yet arrived. Little Edgar couldn't tell his parents what had happened; neither, of course, did the nurse.

On June 24, 1858, Edgar Mortara was seven years old. He was celebrating his birthday with some of his friends. They were playing a game—running about, peeping under furniture and trying to find some object hidden by Edgar's mother. Suddenly the door was thrown open and in walked an officer.

"In the name of the Holy Office, I must take Edgar Mortara with me!" he said gruffly.

Edgar ran to his mother and clung to her skirts.

"Why, no! You can't do this! What right has the Pope to my child?"

"Because," said Anna Morisi, the nurse who had entered behind the officer, "Edgar is a Catholic. He belongs to the Church. I had him baptized when he was three years old."

"You! How dared you!"—Mrs. Mortara shrieked wildly.

But Edgar, crying and kicking, was snatched from his mother's arms, as his mother dropped to the floor in a faint.

What would become of little Edgar Mortara?

The Mortaras went to the highest church officers to try to get Edgar back. They tried to see the Pope. They tried to get to the Cardinal. But it was all in vain. There was one important man for whose help they had not yet asked.

That man was Moses Montefiore. He had become an Elijah, and seemed a Messiah to the Jews. Yes, they would ask Moses Montefiore to do something about it. As soon as they wrote to Sir Moses he promised to try. For any Jew's trouble was also Moses' trouble, and whenever Moses was interested he acted.

Moses Montefiore had been sent to Rome as president of the Jewish Board of Deputies. As usual, he had letters of introduction from the British Secretary.

In Italy, Cardinal Antonelli, one of the high church officers, received Moses Montefiore and greeted him cordially. After the Cardinal had shown him about, Moses sat down and, as usual, came to the point immediately.

"About the Mortara case," Moses said: "Is it possible that any intelligent Christian can allow such a thing to happen? Is it possible that they really will not allow this little Jewish boy, Edgar, to return to his parents?"

Cardinal Antonelli thought a little and then said: "'Non possumus.' We can't help it. We can't do anything about it. The rule of the Church is, once a Catholic always a Catholic. 'Non possumus.'"

Moses then tried to get to the Pope. The Pope, Moses thought, could change any rule. But the Pope wouldn't even allow Moses Montefiore to come to see him. This was the first time that Moses had been unsuccessful in a mission.

Edgar Mortara, the Jewish boy, was brought up a Catholic. Now Sir Moses saw that there was no hope for the Jews in

Europe. More than ever, he realized the need for bringing more and more Jews to Palestine. So he returned to England only long enough to make ready for his visit to Palestine.

*   *   *

England . . . Sir Moses was sitting in his beautiful home in East Cliff Lodge in England. A few friends had come to see him. They tried to persuade Moses not to take the long, hazardous journey to the Holy Land.

Sir Moses, was full of enthusiasm: "It will all happen as our prophets of old foretold. Our people will return to the Holy Land some day. I'm quite certain of that. Then all their troubles will be over."

"But do you suppose, Sir Moses, that the Jews will leave the countries which they have learned to love and call their own?" asked Dr. Lowe, Sir Moses' secretary, as he cleaned his pipe.

"No, of course not, if they love their France or America as I do my England. I don't expect all the Jews to go to live in Palestine, but Palestine must belong to the Jewish people so that all those who must or want to go there, may go there, and Jerusalem will become the center of a Jewish land."

*   *   *

Jerusalem . . . It was decided to start for Jerusalem on Saturday night. They were waiting for the moon to rise in the sky.

At twenty minutes past eleven o'clock they started out for the Holy City. As they were traveling along, calmly and peacefully, Sir Moses remarked,

"Who would believe that one could travel so peacefully along these roads?"

"Yes, because the city is protected by the Turkish Government we need have no fear," said Dr. Lowe.

Just then two Bedouins dashed from behind a rock and galloped up to the carriage.

"Good heaven! We were too hasty with our praise!" exclaimed Sir Moses. "What in the world will they do to us?"

But suddenly Dr. Lowe cried cheerfully: "Sholom aleichem, Rabbi Bezalel, Sholom aleichem, Rabbi David." Then, turning to Sir Moses he said:

"These men are not Bedouins, though they are dressed exactly like Bedouins and ride galloping steeds like those of the Bedouins. They are rabbi-messengers."

As the men pulled in the reins and stood before them they asked in Hebrew, "Where is Sir Moses? How is he? When will he enter Jerusalem? We must hurry back to Jerusalem to give them time to come out to meet him with proper ceremony."

As Sir Moses nodded his head, they saluted him with reverence. Sir Moses, however, did not tell them when he would arrive, because he did not want to inconvenience the inhabitants in any way. The rabbi-messengers saluted again and galloped off, for they intended to be in Jerusalem in the morning.

When Sir Moses and his secretary came near Jerusalem they dismounted, as usual, for a short prayer. Thousands of people were waiting to greet Sir Moses and Lady Montefiore. His Excellency Kemal Pasha, the governor of Jerusalem, sent an escort of horsemen. Representatives of congregations and schools, and the most important citizens had come to meet the travelers. Guns kept firing salutes of welcome. Sir Moses had come with important documents. He received many invitations, but of course he was unable to accept them all. He had one purpose in coming—that was to help the Jews settle in Jerusalem.

His first stop was at one of the colonies which he had helped to set up. In order to see whether the young men were willing to work, Sir Moses announced:

"I should like to have a cistern filled on my estate. But I can't pay much." In a few minutes crowds surrounded him. Dozens wanted a chance to work.

Moses himself then tested eight handicraft-men. "That's the way, young man," Sir Moses said as he tapped one man on the shoulder. "To work with one's hands is very important."

"Why, Sir Moses, the Jews in the Holy Land, work harder, and *like* to work, more even than any in Europe."

"Yes, yes, so I see," Moses said, well pleased. "And I think we shall begin by building houses in Jerusalem."

The young men readily agreed. Sir Moses continued as if telling a dream.

"Each house will have a plot of ground in front of it, large enough to cultivate olive trees, grape vines, and vegetables!"

The young men answered eagerly: "Speedily, speedily and in our day."

"The houses ought to pay a rental," Sir Moses continued. "Then, too, we shall establish a loan society for the poor."

Far into the night Moses Montefiore made clear, practical plans for rebuilding Jerusalem.

When Moses left he took with him two men to study the weaving industry in Preston, England, and thus Moses laid the foundation of a new settlement in Palestine called Ohel Moshe. This work gave Moses more happiness than all the titles he had ever received in England.

*   *   *

London . . . It was the one-hundredth birthday of Moses Montefiore. He was sitting in a corner of the large room in East Cliff Lodge at Ramsgate. Telegrams, flowers and gifts surrounded him. One telegram he prized above all—the one sent by Queen Victoria. When it arrived the serenaders sang "God save the Queen."

The harbor was lit up and bonfires burned throughout the town. All day a procession of visitors filled the room.

Toward evening when there seemed to be a little lull, one of Moses' nephews asked:

"What is this thing, Uncle?" as he pointed to a ring lying in a little jewelry box on the table.

"Oh, just a plain ring. But I like it best because the word *Jerusalem* is engraved on it."

"And this stone?"

"Well, you see that comes from Jerusalem, and I like to keep it under my pillow. On that stone are engraved the words, 'Thy servants take pleasure in her (Jerusalem's) stones and favor the dust thereof.' "

"And these gloves, Uncle—why do you keep them in this case?"

"They will go to Judith, Lady Montefiore College. Those are the gloves I wore when I shook hands with the Russian Czar. What a visit that was . . ."

"I remember . . ." the old man began.

"I remember in Paris when I met King Louis Phillipe . . ."

"I remember in Bucharest—in Morocco."

"I remember in Constantinople . . ."

And indeed Moses Montefiore had lived a full and worthy life. Late into the night he sat telling incidents of that life which will never be forgotten by the Jewish people.

"I remember . . ."

The Second Purim

FATHER TOMASO, a Franciscan monk, was on his way to treat a sick Jew. The Father knew a little about curing the sick, and so he served as doctor to many people in Damascus.

It was a dark night, and the Father's servant had to carry a lantern to light the road. Just as they left the monastery, they met a Mohammedan merchant and his mule driver.

"We consider ourselves lucky to meet anyone on such a dark night, especially a holy Father," said the Mohammedan.

"Whether we know it or not, the Lord always directs our path," replied Father Tomaso.

"Yes, praised be Allah, the God of the Mohammedans, for sending you to direct us."

"But why will you let me direct you only along this sandy road? Why do you not join us Christians and let us direct your whole life?"

The mule driver was gritting his teeth. He wanted to speak,

but his master stopped him. Instead, the merchant said politely:

"We will not become Christians, Father. You need not waste your time. We had better go, each on his own road."

"We had better hurry," Father Tomaso's servant reminded him, "or the Jew whom you want to cure may die."

"I do not think you will save any Mohammedan souls to-night, Father, so you may as well save the Jew if you can," said the merchant.

Having received their directions, the Mohammedan and his driver rode off while the Father and his servant hastened to the house of the Jew.

As soon as the mule-driver and the merchant were alone, the servant spat angrily upon the ground and, patting his donkey on the head, exclaimed: "No one is going to tell me about my religion, is he, Blackey? Sh-sh—I'll tell you a secret!" The driver spoke into the donkey's ear, "This Christian dog shall die by no other hand than my own!"

Meanwhile the Father and his servant had finished their visit to the Jew. As they turned to walk toward the monastery, the servant asked, "Will the Jew live, Father?"

"O, yes, there is nothing serious the matter with him physically. He simply worries too much about what he reads in the newspaper."

"Worries about what he reads in the newspaper?" The servant repeated without understanding the words he had just heard.

Father Tomaso explained: "Well, for instance he reads that in France, in Russia, in fact in almost the whole of Europe they still have special laws against the Jews. And here in the East, too. That hurts this Jew and makes him sick, but only with worry!"

Just then they met the merchant and his driver again. This time Father Tomaso stopped them.

"Well," he asked kindly, "have you found the place you were looking for?"

"O, yes, we have attended to our business. These Jews here are not a bad lot. At least they mind their own affairs. They are not always trying to make us become Jews."

"But your religion won't save you from burning in hell after death," the Father replied.

At this the driver could control himself no longer. He jumped at the Father and slew him. The servant cried desperately, "Father, Father!" And then he, too, was slain.

It was soon discovered at the monastery that Father Tomaso and his servant had not returned. A complete search was made throughout the monastery grounds. The bells sent out a thunderous peal.

Who had murdered Father Tomaso and his servant?

* * *

Since Father Tomaso had been on a visit in the Jewish quarters, the monks decided that it must have been a Jew who killed him.

Soon the Christians, aided by some Mohammedans, were searching the Jewish quarters.

They broke into the synagogues, tore the Scrolls, and cried wildly: "We will find the murderer. Where is he hiding?"

Someone mentioned that the Father had last been seen at a Jewish barber-shop. So the mob rushed into the barber-shop.

"He will tell us who killed the Holy Father, or we will kill him!" they cried.

On no evidence at all the barber was taken to prison and tortured.

The newspaper appeared with the headline: FATHER TOMASO AND HIS SERVANT MURDERED IN THE JEWISH QUARTER OF DAMAScus! "It is nothing new," the news column stated, "in the history of the Jews, to kill Christians for the Passover ceremony. It is clear that the Holy Father was murdered by some Jew who wanted his blood for Passover. Those suspected will be kept in prison and tortured until they confess. Since the Father was a Frenchman, Ratti Menton, the French Consul, will do all in his power to have the Jews punished immediately."

And when the Jews in Europe, and even in America, read the papers, the age-old wail arose: "How long, O Lord, how long?"

And again as in the days of Menasseh ben Israel all the Jews began to unite. They would down this horrible accusation against the Jews! They held meetings and conventions. They sent a delegation to Damascus. They would fight the cause of

the Jews. Meanwhile the Jews in Damascus were being tortured.
Who knew how many would be left alive?

* * *

Never had the French Consul attended to his duty so quickly.
He had the governor of Syria send out an accusation against the
Jews by the Turkish government. Then he called a meeting of
the monks.

At the meeting Father Tusti, one of the monks, said, "We
shall stick to one story—that the Jews killed Father Tomaso.
They needed his blood for Passover, and so they killed him.
The Jews did it, and no others!"

But Ratti Menton was more careful. "There is a story being
told that Father Tomaso quarreled with a Mohammedan merchant. If that is true . . ." he said, scratching his head and
wrinkling his forehead.

But Father Tusti interrupted: "If we all blame the Jews,
everyone will think that they are guilty."

Many Christians were sorry for the Jews, but could do nothing about it. The monks, however, placed the blame on the Jews.

To complete their plan, Ratti Menton had prepared a little
gift for the monks. This was a paper saying that the government
would order the arrest of all Jews. The meeting closed with
everyone satisfied.

* * *

At the same time another incident was taking place in France.

It was a warm spring day. Everything seemed bright and gay.

"Liberty! Equality! Fraternity!" cried three young men who were walking along the street. They spied an organ-grinder.

"Play the *Marseillaise*," they said, and began to sing: "*Allons enfants de la patrie.*" (That is the French national anthem.)

The organ-grinder had a monkey, too, and when the music began the children came running from all sides to see the fun. The monkey held out his little red cap for money. But when the children gave him peanuts instead, he tipped his cap and bowed graciously. Peals of laughter came from the children, and they, too, joined in the singing.

But suddenly in the midst of all the merry-making, a policeman stepped up to the young men and said gruffly. "You are under arrest!"

All joy left the children. It didn't seem real. "They're arrested! They're arrested!" the children kept repeating in their grief.

The young men seemed equally bewildered. They began to speak angrily, and waved their hands in all directions. "What right have you to arrest us? This is now a free republic, isn't it? What was our offense?"

But in spite of all they said the three young men were taken to court.

"We shall go to Adolphe Cremieux," one of the young men said defiantly, "yes, Adolphe Cremieux. *There's* a man who fights for justice."

In the morning session of the French Court, Adolphe Cremieux had just finished pleading a case. His final words were: "Do not condemn a man to death because he has risen against the government. Do not kill a man because he does not agree with the State. No one deserves death for such an offense." There was great applause as Cremieux took up his brief-case and hurried out to meet his friend Solomon Munk, a great Jewish scholar.

As Cremieux came running down the stairs of the court house, he heard the crying of the children. Cremieux could not bear to see anybody cry without wanting to help. He stopped the policeman and heard the whole story. Though Cremieux was late for his appointment, he returned to the court, argued the case and had the young men dismissed.

When Cremieux arrived at the restaurant where he was to meet Solomon Munk, his friend was already there. Cremieux dropped into a chair. His face darkened as he read the headline in the newspaper which Munk held.

"Again that horrible blood accusation!" he cried.

"Yes, my dear Adolphe," replied Solomon Munk, "you have been so busy pleading other causes lately that you have forgotten that you are a Jew."

"I guess I've given too much time to people in general and

not enough to my own people, the Jews," Cremieux answered humbly. "But what can I do about this affair?"

"Read this," said Munk as he handed Cremieux a note. Cremieux read the following:

"To the Rich Jews of Israel:

If you will pay me 20,000 lira I will undertake to defend the Jews of Damascus. I will announce in every European journal that the Jews are innocent. But, if you do not give me this money, then I will add more lies to those already being printed, and I will do all I can to make everybody in Damascus and all Europe believe that the Jews are guilty.

(Signed) Dr. Thilbert."

Munk waited till Cremieux had finished reading the note, and then asked:

"Do you see now what you must do?"

"Yes, Solomon, I myself shall go to Damascus to plead the cause of those innocent Jews. But you must come and act as interpreter, since you have such a complete knowledge of Arabic." Cremieux's eyes glowed. He struck the table with his fist, exclaiming: "This is one time when scoundrels and liars will not be the victors! Justice shall triumph!"

The zeal of the Prophets for justice was burning in the blood of Cremieux, and he threw aside every other interest, so that he might study the *Damascus Affair*.

* * *

The first thing that Cremieux did was to have an interview with Louis Phillipe, the French king. From him he received permission to interview the French Consul, Ratti Menton, his witnesses, and the Jewish prisoners.

Cremieux then went to Damascus where he drew up a statement in which he proved that the Jews had been unjustly accused. This was signed by every foreign consul except Ratti Menton.

"They are coming, they are coming, the three good angels! Clear the road!" shouted a multitude of voices. "Sir Moses Montefiore, Cremieux and Munk! They will deliver the Jews from this accusation, not only now but for ever!"

Queen Victoria had given Sir Moses the use of a special vessel in which to cross the channel. And the three great men made a triumphal march through Europe.

*   *   *

At last the great day arrived! Mohammedans, Christians, and Jews had gathered in the small court house in Damascus. Excitement ran high.

When Adolphe Cremieux came before the bar there fell upon the room such a deep silence that one could have heard a pin drop. Without further ado, he called one of Ratti's witnesses and asked:

QUESTION: Did you see a Jew kill this monk, Father Tomaso?
ANSWER: No—but I heard——
QUESTION: Thank you, that is all I wanted to know.

TODROS
GELLER

The next witness arose and Cremieux asked:

QUESTION: Did the Jews do anything unusual that night?

ANSWER: No, they closed the gates as usual, but on that night they said, "Let us shut the gates and let us not go out, because there is danger outside."

QUESTION: Did you hear them say those words?

ANSWER: No, but they must have, because none walked out that night.

A little titter passed through the court from Christians and Mohammedans as well as from Jews. Then Cremieux asked that the Jewish barber be brought in. The barber, pale and exhausted, could hardly stand on his feet.

"Tell us the story as you know it," said Cremieux kindly.

Pulling himself together with all his strength the barber began:

"They broke into my house and they insisted that I tell them about the murder. But I couldn't. I couldn't because I knew nothing about it. Then Ratti Menton ordered that I be given the bastinado—that is 500 blows with a stick upon the soles of the feet." The barber pointed to his feet. "Five hundred," he repeated. "I thought I should die. I couldn't stand it any longer." The barber began to weep.

"Then," he continued, "Ratti Menton came up to me and said, 'David Arari killed the Father, didn't he?' And I answered, 'Yes, David Arari.' Forgive me, M. Cremieux, I was a coward. Then Menton asked again, 'And Moses Abulafia helped him, didn't he?' And I said, 'Yes, Moses Abulafia!' O, M. Cremieux, I was afraid and sick, and I didn't know what I was talking about." By now the barber's voice became a whisper, for he had no more strength. "And I also named Moses Salonika," the barber whispered, "and a whole list of other names."

Someone gave the barber a glass of water. Then Cremieux encouraged him to continue.

"O, M. Cremieux, I was afraid. Forgive me. Please, I couldn't help it."

By now all the Jews and some Mohammedans, too, were weeping.

Cremieux had worked hard. He had found out all that Ratti Menton had done to the Jews in trying to make them confess.

Cremieux turned to David Arari, another prisoner, and said: "Tell these people about the tortures you endured."

David Arari advanced to the witness stand and said, in a low voice: "Menton kept us without food or drink for 36 hours, nor were we allowed to go to sleep for 36 hours."

"That's enough," Cremieux said kindly, and David Arari stepped down. Cremieux then turned to Menton and said:

"Is it true, that you ordered a search for Father Tomaso in the Jewish Quarter? And that when a youth told you that Father Tomaso had been seen speaking to a certain merchant just before he was killed, you hushed up that evidence?"

Menton grew pale. His knees began to tremble under him. He looked as if he would fall. Cremieux continued:

"But you did take as proof anything these people said when they were tortured—these people, who you knew were sick with pain and wanted only to be allowed to die."

Then Cremieux turned to the people in the court room and pleaded: "Friends: it would take weeks to tell how the Jews were tortured to make them confess a crime which they did not commit. Meanwhile our people are being persecuted. The mobs are breaking into the synagogues and tearing the holy scrolls, and who will stop them?"

A sigh arose from the Jews in the room. "Who will stop them?" they murmured.

"Must we suffer this over and over again?" Cremieux continued:

The English Consul rose and said: "No. In the name of seven countries, we here protest this cruel and unjust treatment of the Jews."

The governor heard what was happening and quickly sent a *firman,* a proclamation freeing the Jews from prison, and allowing them all to go back to their homes.

Amid loud hand-clapping and shouts of joy the prisoners were carried out of the prison on the shoulders of their friends.

There was great rejoicing in Damascus. The people cried: "A second Purim! A second Purim!"

And it was a second Purim indeed! Cremieux, Montefiore and Munk had won the freedom of the Jews.

For Liberty

December 17th, 1938, was a cold, slushy day in Philadelphia.

"There's nothing to do outside, there's nothing to do outside today," Avi chanted his usual song.

"For once you are right," his mother smiled, "why don't you and your friends try that new game that Uncle Manny sent you for Chanukko?"

"Yippee," Avi called out as he and his friends clambered up the steps to his room.

They took out the new game and sprawled on the floor.

"What's the name of it?" Noam asked as he looked over Avi's shoulder. But he himself quickly read the answer: "*Magic Finance!* That must be something like *Monopoly*," Noam decided.

Avi continued to read: "Magic Finance, or Bills of Exchange."

116

"I'll have to bring over my dictionary," Daniel joined in. "Here are the directions. These might help." And Avi continued to read:

"Here is a game of skill and chance, for old and young. The disc is divided into little squares, representing towns, rivers, etc., famous at the time of the Revolutionary War. In addition there is the Little Office on Front Street, Philadelphia, where Hayim Salomon sat and just seemed to coin money for the War to go on. Near him is the office of Robert Morris, the Superintendent of Finance during the Revolution. In the center there is the Hall of Independence and near it a deck of cards.

"Each player takes a block called "Colonist" and places it at the starting point in New York Bay. Each player then receives bills of exchange (cards) of different value from $1.00 to $1,000.00. All begin in New York Bay. The aim, of course, is to get Freedom. That can be gotten by reaching the Hall of Independence."

Avi suddenly interrupted himself, "O, I'm tired of reading. Let's play!"

"All right, a dozen cards to each and let's go!"

"Let Avi begin, because it's his game," Daniel suggested.

"Second," Noam called quickly; and that left Daniel third.

Avi picked a card from the center and read: "I am Hayim Salomon, a broker, but I serve the government. I work for liberty and freedom. That's my real business. Put me in my office in Front St., near the Coffee House."

Avi moved his Colonist to the Coffee House and put the card back on the bottom of the deck. "A funny business," Avi thought, but said nothing.

Noam then picked his card and read, "I am a broker, a man who makes a living by buying bills of exchange. I am here to make money, not to fight for liberty."

"That's a tough broker," said Daniel.

Noam paid no attention to the interruption and continued to read. "Pay $6.00 and you may escape from the Provost, that British prison."

"Suppose I don't pay," Noam objected.

"Then you will remain in prison. And I suppose that's not any too pleasant," Daniel answered.

"Come on. Is this a discussion or a game?" Avi asked impatiently.

Noam paid the broker and left the prison.

Next Daniel picked his card. "We are the hungry, ragged soldiers in Valley Forge. No shoes on our feet, no clothes on our backs. Go to the bank of Robert Morris and get 50 bills of exchange."

The game seemed to become more interesting. Avi took his card and read: "I am Robert Morris, always running to my friend the broker, Hayim Salomon, for money. Take $10,000."

Avi, with a delighted "Yippee" made the move.

Noam took his card and read, "I am James Madison, starving to death. Go to Hayim Salomon. He will give me $500."

Noam, too, was glad to get some money for a change and out rang the "Yippee" as he made the move.

Daniel lost no time. He read from his card, "You have a big loss at sea. All your bills of exchange drop $10.00."

Daniel sorrowfully moved 10 squares away from the Hall of Independence.

"I guess I won't get my liberty," Daniel sighed.

"And nobody will," chimed in Noam. "This Hayim Salomon seems to keep his place, though he keeps giving away so much."

"That's because he understands how to use those bills of exchange," Avi explained.

"He seems to have had an important part in helping win the American Revolutionary War," Noam suggested.

"Say, Avi, do you have that new book, *The Great March, Book II*? There is a story in there about Hayim Salomon that will help us understand this game."

"First, let us finish with these cards," Avi objected. "Then we'll read the story."

When the game was over, Avi walked over to the bookcase and said, with an air of pride, which he tried to hide, "Here's the new book!"

Daniel looked through the table of contents and cried, " 'For Liberty'—that's it!" He began to read aloud, and this was the story that he read:

"Fire, fire!" the word passed quickly from mouth to mouth.

There was no fire gong to sound, and there were no fire engines to send out. The firemen arrived in their horse-driven wagon, and began to work.

"How did it start?" everybody wondered. These were war times, and everybody was under suspicion.

Hayim Salomon, the Polish Jew, was paler than usual. He sat behind his desk in his little store in New York. His wife was talking angrily:

"Why should you get mixed up in this war? It was enough that you fought under those Polish leaders, Pulaski and the others."

"Rachel, dear, please don't talk that way. It's in my blood to fight oppression wherever I see it. How much more do I want to do it for America, the country in which I have found freedom and opportunity."

"You're a broker and an auctioneer. Your business is to make a living for your family. You may lend some money to the government if you charge a proper interest for it, as others do. But that is all that is necessary."

Salomon looked at her and felt pity in his heart because she couldn't understand.

"Then, besides," Mrs. Salomon continued, determined to have her say, "you had to join that group called Sons of Liberty. Now you will be suspected of everything, whether you do it or not!"

Suddenly there was a knock at the door, and in marched two

British soldiers. Each laid a hand on Hayim and said, "You are under arrest, suspected of sending fire boats down the New York harbor."

Rachel began to cry.

"Don't worry, Rachel," Hayim said in his usual gentle tone, "it will all turn out for the best."

And Hayim took hasty leave of his wife.

* * *

"Right—right—right—right—left—left—left—left."

As they approached the prison corridor the words became clearer: "Left—left—left." Then right—right—right—etc. It wasn't a command; it was just the same word, repeated by different voices. Just then one of the guards opened the door.

"Here," he said, as he shoved Hayim into a small, stuffy room. "Make yourself comfortable." And the guard locked the door behind him.

Hayim tripped over a body lying at his feet.

"Excuse me," Hayim said hastily.

"Aw, that's all right, young fellow," said a weak voice. "Don't worry about me. I'll be dead soon."

The prisoners were lying on a cold, damp floor, packed close together like sardines in a tin. Salomon saw no possible space for himself.

One soldier, who noticed his expression, said kindly: "Don't worry, fella', always room for another."

Hayim at last wriggled himself into a space on the floor. The bare planks cut into his flesh. Hayim turned toward the left. He heard each prisoner pass the word, "left." And as he said it, each one turned toward the left. Hayim turned back toward the right. Again word was passed along, "right." All turned toward the right. At last a voice cried:

"Make up your mind, will you? Will it be left or right? And stay put."

Then Salomon realized that the prisoners were lying so close together that when one wanted to turn, all the others had to turn also. All had to turn when one turned. So the word "left" or "right" was passed down the row when anyone turned. That was what he had heard outside the prison cells.

Though his bones ached, he dared not turn again. Instead, he spoke to his neighbor.

"How long does one usually stay here?"

"Me no can spik mucha English," came the reply.

"Oh, you're an Italian," Hayim said cheerfully, as if he had met a long lost friend. And Hayim continued the conversation in Italian.

Then turning his head—only his head, slightly to the other side, he said: "Can you imagine treating human beings like this? But it must be good to die for liberty."

The neighbor answered: "Bitte ich verstehe das English nicht so gut." And Hayim continued the conversation in German. Suddenly a voice called out:

"It don't feel so good to die here for anything. But say, I'd like to know how many languages you can speak?"

Hayim addressed himself to the Voice: "I can speak English, German, Italian——"

"Stop your foolin'! You can get out of this dump on much less than that!"

"French, Polish and Russian," Hayim finished, after the interruption.

"Gee—then you won't die for Liberty."

In a few days everybody in the prison had heard about Hayim Salomon and his knowledge of languages.

Heister, the English general, was pleased with his discovery.

"What a find," he thought. "Just to think that this man might have perished in prison." Now he would have someone who could understand and speak to the hired German soldiers, known as the Hessians. Then, too, this Jew could understand the French soldiers who joined the American colonists in their war for independence. Little did Heister realize what Hayim would do with his knowledge of German and French.

* * *

"Who goes there?" the sentry spoke into the foggy night.

"It's only I, Hayim Salomon. I couldn't sleep so I thought I would come out and talk a bit with you."

"Very glad to have you." The guard motioned Hayim to sit down on the bench.

Hayim felt that now he had the chance of his life. He had always tried to do something for freedom. So he said to the guards,

"What are you Hessians doing here in America? You know the English are oppressing these colonies. They won't let them trade with other countries. They are taking their freedom from them. And what do you do? You come here and help the English." The Hessian guards fidgeted uncomfortably on the benches.

"Aren't you ashamed of yourselves? You should leave this place immediately! Give up this business of killing men, especially these innocent people fighting for their freedom!"

"Well—you—see—we didn't think,—that—way," one of the soldiers stammered an excuse.

"Yes, I understand," Hayim said kindly, "but now you must act. Here, I will pay your fare back to Germany. Tell the others I will do the same for them." The guards took the money and promised to leave.

Heister noticed that, little by little, the Hessian soldiers were leaving the English army. There were few Hessians and fewer prisoners. What was happening? Heister asked his advisers. Who was doing this? But no one suspected the slight, delicate-looking Jew, Hayim Salomon.

At the end of a few weeks many prisoners were missing. Had so many died? Or was Hayim helping them to escape?

*   *   *

"He is bringing down the rate of interest!" said Mr. Chaloner, a broker, as he entered the Little Coffee House on Front Street, in Philadelphia.

"And he will ruin us," shouted another, and his eyes flashed fire.

"Yes, we shall die at the hands of this little Jew, Hayim Salomon!"

"Only yesterday he lent $10,000 to Robert Morris without any interest or was it ½ of 1%?"

"And on what security?" flashed another.

"None—there is none. I say, he is a queer man!"

Just then they noticed Hayim sitting in his usual corner, quiet and courteous, observing everything. In Salomon's presence the brokers grew silent.

They came over to Salomon's table, and Mr. Chaloner the broker, who sold the bills of exchange for any price that he could get, asked: "Mr. Salomon, for how much do you expect to sell these new bills of exchange that have come from France?"

"I don't know for how much, but I do know I will not sell them for less than they are marked."

John Chaloner spoke again, "Mr. Salomon, don't you realize that people will not pay so much for this paper? Don't you see that it is to your interest to sell them for anything you can get for them?"

"Or," added another broker, "maybe you are in this business for the glory of the government—for Liberty, Freedom and

Independence?" The man lifted his hands and raised his voice as if he were making a speech.

To this Mr. Salomon replied by taking a letter out of his pocket. "Read this," he said.

"Our soldiers are dying for want of food. They have been in rags for months; and they have stood that. But they will not go without food. Some troops have already mutinied. Send whatever you can."

Mr. Salomon gazed searchingly at each man. "How do you suppose we shall win this war? Dead men can't fight. And living ones must be kept alive."

"Oh, *you* will finance the Revolution!" Mr. Chaloner laughed. "Ha, ha, that's quite a different matter. In that case, I shall send Robert Morris and James Madison to you. They want to get money for nothing. I shall tell them that I have found the good angel."

"You needn't trouble," Hayim Salomon answered, still gently. "They have already been here; and a few others about whom you don't know."

"But, Mr. Salomon, how do you always manage to have money in the Bank of North America? We are told you are the largest depositor. That's a puzzle."

"That's not so difficult, once you realize that I am fighting to get Liberty, and not money for my children." Then, Hayim added somewhat impatiently, "I suppose I do know a little more about money than you do."

The brokers had hoped to persuade Salomon to charge the same amount of interest as they did. But when they heard his replies they just shrugged their shoulders hopelessly. "He's not a broker. He's an idealist," one said, "I wonder! Maybe I have not been fair to the Jews!"

* * *

Hayim hurried home. It was the eve of the great fast day, Yom Kippur. He washed himself hurriedly and ate dinner before sunset according to the custom. Then he took his talis (the prayer shawl) and the special holiday prayer-book and went to the synagogue with his wife.

Seated in the synagogue, Hayim forgot all the troubles of the war. He forgot all about the bills of exchange. He forgot about lending money. He thought of one thing only: he was to pray to God for forgiveness of his sins. He was to pray to God to grant the Jews and America and the whole world a "Happy New Year."

Soon the congregation had gathered and the cantor began to intone the famous Kol Nidre prayer. "Kol—Nid—Re . . ."

The cantor sang the *Kol Nidre* once. The women wept and the men swayed back and forth in their "talesim." The Cantor sang the *Kol Nidre* twice. When he began to sing it for the third time (for it is the custom to repeat the *Kol Nidre* three times) a great commotion arose in the synagogue. Two soldiers had entered and demanded to see Hayim Salomon. The

beadle and a few members of the synagogue could not hold them back.

They marched down the aisle to Hayim's seat and handed him a note from General Washington which read, "Unless you send $40,000 immediately, we shall have to surrender; then we shall be slaves forever!"

Hayim was bewildered. "But how!" he exclaimed. "Where can I get such a large sum, and on this night, too?"

Then, as if fired by a sudden thought he removed his prayer shawl and walked up to the cantor's stand.

"Friends, I have just received a message from George Washington. He tells me that unless we raise $40,000 immediately, the war will be lost. I know that this is Yom Kippur Eve—the holiest night of the year. I know the *Kol Nidre* service is the most solemn of the year, and should not be interrupted. Still, friends, I beg you to understand how grave is our problem. If we lose this war, we lose not only thousands of lives, but we give up liberty and freedom for ourselves and our children. If we fail now, our children shall be slaves forever. I say, let us pledge this sum here and now. I myself shall give $15,000."

The congregation stared wide-eyed as some of the most pious Jews, moved by Salomon's speech, offered thousands of dollars.

"We shall not hand our children over to Pharoah," one cried with enthusiasm.

"We shall help this country, which has given a haven of refuge to the Jews."

"We shall give our last penny even on Yom Kippur, for liberty and freedom."

Amidst great excitement the $40,000 was raised. The congregation then returned to its prayers. The Jews felt that they had made the day even holier by pledging themselves to the sacred cause of liberty and freedom.

*   *   *

As Daniel finished reading, Avi and Noam applauded. They liked the story. Now, they thought, they could play the game much better. And they began the game all over again.

The Good Fairy

"I SHALL be Judah Maccabee, the leader of the Jews," said Simon Gratz, the oldest of the Gratz family. "Benjamin, Richea, and Rebecca will be the Jews. Hyman, Joseph, Jacob, and Rachel will be the Greeks."

"Oh, no," cried pretty Rachel as her black eyes twinkled. "Oh no, I won't be a Greek!" she pouted.

"Aw, Rachel, this is only a game," urged Simon.

"I don't care, game or no game, I will not be mixed up with the Greeks," Rachel insisted.

"All right, Rachel dear," spoke up gentle, unselfish Rebecca, "you take my place. I'll be the Greek instead of you."

"Becky," said Simon, "you shouldn't do that! You always give up everything for someone else."

"I don't mind. I even like to," said Becky sweetly.

And the Greeks began the attack on the Jews.

Meanwhile Michael Gratz, an important business man, called the "Merchant Prince," was walking down a quiet Philadelphia street. All the houses on the block were of the same size, pattern and color; pressed brick fronts, white or green shutters and marble steps. He greeted the neighbors as they sat in front of their houses reading their newspapers before the evening meal.

"Good evening, Mr. Jones," he said to the man next door.

"Good evening," replied his neighbor. "Did you notice that they've finished placing the new street lights?"

"Yes indeed," chuckled Mr. Gratz, "looks just like London now."

Michael Gratz was very proud of the city's growth, for he had done much to help it.

Mr. Gratz soon reached his own home and lifted the brass knocker. No servant had to open the door in the evening when Mr. Gratz was expected. There was a mad scramble to meet him. Even the last battle between the Greeks and the Jews was left unfought. Each child wanted to be the first in his father's arms. And all of them began at once to tell of the day's events. "I ate,"—"I found,"—"I broke,"—"I made"—Mr. Gratz could really not make out what any of them was trying to say.

At the dinner table, especially as this was Friday night, and *Chanukko,* each had a chance to tell his story. Everyone had some report or some complaint; everyone except Rebecca.

"And what have you done today, Rebecca?" Rebecca blushed prettily and answered, "Oh, nothing special."

"If she were to tell what she did," Jack answered for her,

"she would sound as if she were bragging. She is always looking out for the rest of us, and is always making peace between us."

"She'll be the president of some big organization for the advancement of peace, some day," said Simon, proud of the long words he knew.

Just then the knocker sounded. The servant brought in a special delivery letter and handed it to Mr. Gratz. Everybody looked on while he opened it. As his eyes passed over the words, his face grew suddenly pale.

"What is it?" asked his wife, breathlessly.

"A letter from your sister Shinah," replied Mr. Gratz.

"Read it. Read it aloud."

Mr. Gratz began slowly, in a low tone:

"Dear Loved Ones:

"I shall not be able to spend Shabbos Chanukko with you, as we had planned. It grieves me, but I think it will be best for all of us. You see, I've just married the man I love—and he does not belong to our faith. He is a Gentile.

"Please ask Father to forgive me.

"Love,

Shinah."

For a moment none moved or spoke. Grandfather Simon looked as if someone had struck him a heavy blow. Then he said brokenly:

"She was right not to come. I shall never forgive her."

The Chanukko gaiety was spoiled. A hush fell upon the household. The joking, the riddles and the singing ceased. Each child found some quiet corner. Rebecca went up to her room and cried herself to sleep. And she never forgot what Grandpa Simon had said, nor how shocked and sad he had looked.

* * *

Rebecca Gratz, secretary of "The Female Association for the Relief of Women and Children in Reduced Circumstances," was reading the minutes:

"Dr. Mease, in his speech at our last meeting, said: 'Not money, but necessities were given. Everybody in Philadelphia appreciates the good work of your society.'"

Just as her brother Simon had foretold, Rebecca had become a leader in many charitable clubs. She, however, was the secretary and not the president. That meant hard work and few honors.

Rebecca finished reading the minutes and sat down. But she did not have the accustomed interest in the business at hand. Contrary to her usual habit, she kept fumbling with a card in her note-book. She read the card and smiled. Then she wrote a few notes, looked at the card and smiled again. It was clear that she was thinking of something far away.

"My, but this meeting is lasting long!" Rebecca thought. At last she heard the words, "The meeting stands adjourned." Again, contrary to her habit, she impatiently rushed to get her coat and was waving good-bye hurriedly when Mrs. Hodges, one of the members, called:

"Wait a minute, Rebecca, I'll walk with you."

Then, when they had walked a little way she said: "Well, well, Rebecca dear, I just wonder whether it's that card you were reading that made you so impatient."

Rebecca blushed and smiled. "Yes, I guess I was in a hurry to get away, because I am going to the Dancing Assembly tonight." She took the card from the book and showed it to her friend.

Mrs. Hodges read and smiled. "Oh! so it's Samuel Ewing. Well, I don't blame you. He is so clever and charming."

"Yes, I think he is a very worthy son of Dr. Ewing, the first president of the University of Pennsylvania."

"Here we are at your door. I hope you will have an enjoyable evening."

Rebecca lifted the knocker. She could hardly wait for the door to be opened.

As she entered her mother asked affectionately, "Now who is it tonight, Washington or Samuel?"

"It may be neither," answered Rebecca, as she ran up the stairs and began to dress for the great event.

Her slender figure soon flitted down the stairs. Her dark hair curled about a fair, delicate face with almost perfectly modelled features. Her light green dress with its billowing hoops set off her frail beauty.

"Well! Here is where the Society for the Relief of Children

in Reduced Circumstances loses its secretary," Simon teased.

"So they will get a much better one," came the quick reply.

"But what will happen to all those fancy ideas about a Fuel Society, and the Sunday School for the children and the Asylum for the Orphans in Philadelphia?" Simon still pressed.

Just then carriage wheels stopped before the house, and a tall, well-dressed young man entered. Rebecca glanced admiringly at the ruffled shirt and the fancy vest, the powdered hair and the gleaming silver buckles on his shoes.

After Simon and Ewing had exchanged greetings Rebecca rose and bowed gracefully to Ewing. "We had better go immediately," Rebecca smiled, "otherwise my family will tell you what a bad girl I am."

"Oh, I have already found that out for myself," answered Ewing as he looked fondly at Rebecca.

They were about to leave when the knocker sounded and Washington Irving, the author of the *Sketch Book,* entered.

"Of all people!" Rebecca called excitedly, "Where is your friend Matilda?"

"She isn't well. She isn't well at all."

All the joy left Rebecca's eyes and heart. She asked Samuel to excuse her from the dance. The excitement of the day, the hopes of the meeting, had fled.

Before Samuel had a chance to reply, Washington urged, "Please don't let that interfere with your dance. You will come over tomorrow."

Samuel looked at Rebecca, his love in his eyes. As he helped her into the coach he said, "O Rebecca, you are not only beautiful and charming, but good and kind too. How long shall we continue this way? You know that Matilda Hoffman cannot live." Rebecca shuddered at the thought. "And then Washington Irving will want to marry you."

"Oh no, there was never such a thought between us."

"Please, Rebecca, will you marry me?"

"Don't you know that that is impossible? You are a Gentile and I am a Jew. I like you very much, perhaps more than any of my friends, but I cannot marry you."

"So I shall go on being your friend just like Washington Irving and Maria and Matilda Hoffman and the others—and nothing more?"

"Nothing more?" Rebecca questioned in surprise. "Haven't we been happy this way?"

Early next morning, after a sleepless night, Rebecca hastened to the bedside of Matilda Hoffman, the girl whom Washington Irving loved. Matilda was dying of tuberculosis. Rebecca, without fear for herself nursed Matilda for many weeks, but in the end Matilda died in Rebecca's arms.

In his sorrow Washington Irving looked to Rebecca for comfort. He came so often and stayed so long that the big, airy room on the second floor of the large Gratz house came to be known as "The Washington Irving Room."

But soon after the death of Matilda, Irving decided to leave the States. One afternoon he came to say good-bye to Rebecca. She had been upstairs, nursing her grandfather.

"You know, Rebecca," Irving said, "since I finished the *Sketch Book* I haven't written a thing."

"When you are out of the States you will feel better." It was very difficult for Rebecca to give this advice. Her friend Matilda was dead, and Samuel Ewing had married a Gentile. Rebecca needed a devoted friend as much as Irving did. Still, she advised Irving without a thought for herself.

"You are so good, so kind and considerate, Rebecca. You don't seem real. You seem to have stepped out of a fairy tale," Irving said fondly.

Rebecca blushed. "Your imagination makes you exaggerate."

There was a pause in the conversation. Irving thought not only of Rebecca's kindness and unselfishness. "How heroic it is," he thought, "for a girl to give up marrying the man she loves because he is of a different religion."

Irving heaved a deep sigh and said, "I know I shall miss you in Scotland. Good-bye, dear Rebecca." And Washington Irving was gone too.

Rebecca ran back upstairs to Grandfather Simon.

"Rebecca," he said: "Bring all my children and grandchildren to me. I want to see them all before I die."

That evening they gathered about his bedside. He asked each child what special thing he should like.

When Rebecca's turn came, she said tearfully, "Please, Grandpa, forgive Aunt Shinah."

"Send for her," the sick man commanded. And he died in Shinah's arms.

*   *   *

Rebecca continued to work steadily. She organized all the societies about which her brother had teased her.

It was March, 1838. Many carriages stopped in front of the Mikveh Israel Synagogue on Broad and York Streets in Philadelphia. Hundreds of people were going to the meeting of the Hebrew Sunday School Society.

As Rebecca Gratz stepped from one of the carriages, a gentleman came up. "Rebecca," he whispered.

"Washington Irving! When did you arrive? How are you? How glad I am to see you!"

He, bowing, kissed her hand and said, "Rebecca, you are lovelier than ever!"

Then he handed her a package, saying, "I thought I might see you here. I've brought you a gift. It's a book—a new book by my friend Sir Walter Scott. He called it *Ivanhoe*. The heroine is a girl named Rebecca. Read it and tell me whether you recognize that girl."

She took the book and smiled her "Thank you."

Then, seeing her start toward the synagogue, he pressed her hand, saying:

"Now I must go. Good-bye."

She watched him hurry away. Then she walked slowly up the steps of the synagogue.

Within, it was cheerful and bright. And so was Rebecca as she walked down the aisle and up the steps of the dais, while the organ played. Rebecca had not married, but she felt like a bride, a bride of the Torah, for Rebecca spent her life teaching the children to study the Torah. Rebecca stood there beautifully charming, happy as she read the prayer which she herself had written for the occasion:

"Come ye children, hearken, hearken unto me and I will teach you the fear of the Lord. Lift up your young hearts in prayer, in all your ways acknowledge Him, and He will direct your paths.

"O God, give unto us the help we need, give us bread to eat and raiment to put on, and instruction to understand Thy mercies. May we be grateful for all Thy goodness, dutiful to our parents, honest in all our dealings, true in our words and actions, affectionate in our behavior to one another, attentive to our teachers and above all, devoted to Thee alone, the God of our fathers, Abraham, Isaac and Jacob."

With these exercises of the Hebrew Sunday School Society the first Hebrew Sunday School in the United States had opened.

He Frees His Slaves

"War, War!" the newsboy cried. "Extra, extra, America declares war on England!"

Judah Touro, a stout, kindly Jew, was having lunch at the home of his friend, Rezin Shepherd. The two men glanced at each other, as the blood left their faces.

"So it has really come!" Touro said at last.

Mr. Shepherd turned to the slave standing at his side and asked: "Did he say, 'war,' John? War between the United States and England!"

"Yes, Sah, Marse Shepherd—them wuz his very words, 'Wah—Wah.'"

Judah Touro sprang from his seat. "You'll have to excuse me, Rezin, I must hurry to the store to settle accounts. I'm expecting a heavy shipload of soap, candles, and codfish in a few days. My New England friends have been very kind to me. I guess it is because they remember me as an honest fellow in my

Uncle Hay's home in Newport. I shall leave you a check for what I owe and you will pay them for the new shipload."

"I—I," Mr. Shepherd blurted, without understanding. "What do you mean?"

"I'm going to enlist. I'm going to fight for New Orleans with my last drop of blood!"

"But Judah, why you? You have important business to attend to. Wait until the younger, the less important . . ."

Without letting his friend complete the sentence, Judah interrupted, smiling: "How do you know who is more and who is less important? Good-bye, dear Rezin, do come over in the evening, and we'll straighten matters out."

As Judah was leaving he stopped and slipped a gift into the hand of Mr. Shepherd's slave. It was a hundred dollar bill.

"Why, Mr. Touro!" the slave cried in surprise, as his eyeballs rolled in their sockets. "Why, Mr. Touro! I won' nevah haf to work no mo'."

"That'll be fine," Touro smiled, as he hurried away.

"Perhaps that shipload has arrived," Touro thought, as he quickly made his way down to the harbor. At the wharves there was a constant bustle. Every size and type of vessel could be found on the river.

"Good afternoon, Mr. Touro. Heard the news yet?"

Judah Touro nodded without speaking.

"Well, Mr. Touro, why so downcast? You won't have to go to battle."

"No, no, of course not," Judah answered.

He walked to one of the windows and learned that his shipment had not arrived. So he quickly made his way down the brick footpath along the shore to his store.

"Joseph," he said to his only clerk, "get down the books and let us go over the accounts now."

"Four days to go yet before the end of the month, Sir, if I may remind you."

"Yes, I know, but we must begin our checking immediately." Joseph asked no more questions and did as he was told.

"You will write down each item of expense. I'll begin to list the items that came in." And Mr. Touro and his clerk began to work over their books. They worked silently for over an hour. Then Mr. Touro looked up and asked:

"Well, what did you get, Joseph?"

"Twenty thousand dollars."

"Good. Then I'll be able to pay before I go."

Joseph looked up in surprise, questioningly. He did not know where Mr. Touro was going.

Just then a boy threw a circular into the store as he announced: "Auction, at Four P.M. o'clock. Auction of the old Universalist Church."

Judah left his books and hurried to the church.

It was a dreary November day. The sun was beginning to set. The round ball of gold cast a halo about the group of people. The auctioneer with the gavel in his hand stood on a raised platform calling "$15,000—$15,000—going—going—$18,000. Who bids more?"

Suddenly a voice was heard from the rear, "$20,000." The auctioneer in a louder tone began all over again: "$20,000, who bids more! $20,000—going—going—gone for $20,000!" And down came the gavel on the stand in front of him.

There was a commotion and quick whispering.

Mr. Touro, the Jewish merchant, had paid $20,000 for the church! Now the church would be turned into a business house! Some wept at the thought.

"Mr. Touro, here is the bill of sale. Let me congratulate you on the fine piece of property you have bought!" said Mr. Clapp, the minister, as he came over to Mr. Touro.

While Judah Touro was writing the check, Mr. Clapp continued, "It is a most excellent site for business."

"Mr. Clapp, I am a friend of religion, and I shall not tear down the church in order that I may get rich. Here, I shall make you a gift of the deed. Your congregation may continue to worship, as heretofore."

Having disposed of the $20,000 Judah rushed back to his store. The clerk was now adding up Mr. Touro's charity expenses. He was reading the items aloud as he wrote them down:

1. Old Stone Mill of Newport (built by Norsemen. Will be given as a historic landmark to the town) . $2,000.
2. First Synagogue in New Orleans (First payment) . . . . $3,000.

3. Seamen's Home . . . . $5,000.
4. Palestine (First contribution for building outside of
   Old Jerusalem Walls) . . . . $10,000.

Mr. Touro walked in quietly and stood by smiling. Then he began in a sing-song voice:

"So that all adds up to——"

Joseph looked up and blushingly answered, "Twenty thousand dollars, plus your other charities. That leaves you five dollars for the rest of the month."

Joseph fidgeted in his seat and began haltingly: "Mr. Touro, may I say, to have so little left at the end of a month, after you have had such large profits, that is being a little too kind, isn't it?"

"But that is why I earn so much. Don't you remember your Bible, 'Cast thy bread upon the waters for thou shalt find it after many days.'" And Judah Touro beamed at the thought of all the good deeds he had done. He swelled with joy, but not with pride, as he said, "Now I can go and let the United States army pay for my meals."

Joseph threw down his pen as he stared wide-eyed at Mr. Touro. "Oh—oh—so that's where you're going!"

That night Mr. Touro enlisted in the army.

*   *   *

Rezin Shepherd took care of Mr. Touro's business as best he could. He freed Mr. Touro's personal slave and gave him a large sum of money in addition, as Mr. Touro had asked him to do.

On a cold January afternoon a headline appeared in the newspapers: JUDAH TOURO, WELL-KNOWN MERCHANT AND PHILANTHROPIST, DEAD. KILLED BY A TEN POUND SHOT WHILE CARRYING AMMUNITION TO THE BATTERY.

And the whole country wept the loss of Judah Touro.

Rezin Shepherd, his friend, went to recover the body. He found Judah severely wounded, but not dead. Mr. Shepherd nursed him tenderly back to life.

By spring Judah Touro's leg was still in a cast, but he was attending to his affairs. He began to put his money into ships and real estate. Again the neighborhood began to tell time by Judah's goings and comings, for he was as punctual as a clock.

One day the knocker on the door of Mr. Touro's home was heard. Joseph, the clerk, opened the door, since Judah's only slave had been freed.

Mr. Shepherd entered briskly as usual, and said breezily, "How are you, Joseph, this bright morning?"

"Very well, thank you, I'm fine, I'm fine," Joseph answered as he looked gravely at Mr. Shepherd. Joseph put his index finger up to his temple and to show the condition of Mr. Touro's mind, kept on twirling his finger. "I don't want to be disrespectful, but he is now offering to add ten thousand dollars to ten thousand dollars already contributed by Amos Lawrence, to erect the Bunker Hill Monument."

Shepherd smiled as he entered Touro's room. Judah arose, beaming, and said, "At last that Bunker Hill Monument will be completed, friend Rezin." Again Judah's eyes were twinkling with joy.

"So it's true!" Shepherd called out, as he recited:

Christian and Jew
  They carried out a plan,
For though of different faith,
  Each is, at heart, a man.

Then he looked down at Touro and asked: "What will you do next?"

"I shall build new walls around the old Newport Cemetery," came the ready answer.

"Judah, you make me laugh. Why, there won't be anything left for me to do."

"Oh, you can still free all your slaves and help them become independent human beings!"

"I shall do that," Shepherd replied with determination. "But I shall let the world know that you set the example."

You see, Judah Touro loved his America as much as his forefathers had loved their Spain.

Who Will Build Ararat?

"COME, look at this picture," called Abraham Seixas to his older brother Judah. Abraham pointed to a picture in the *National Advocate*. It showed Mordecai Manuel Noah, the major general of the militia and the consul of Tunis, coming out of a Noah's Ark.

"Isn't it funny? What would Mr. Noah do with so many animals and that Ark?"

"If you will keep quiet a minute I'll tell you what it is all about."

Judah took the newspaper and glanced down the column. Then Judah, with an air of knowing it all, asked, "Do you remember the story of Noah in the Bible?"

"Of course I do. The flood came and Noah took his family and the animals, two of each kind, into the Ark."

Abraham would have continued, but Judah interrupted by asking: "But what happened at the end?"

"The flood went down and those who were with Noah rested on Mount Ararat." Abraham felt proud of his Sunday School knowledge.

"Good. Now then, Mordecai Manuel Noah, like Noah in the Bible wants to build an Ararat, a haven for the Jewish people. He wants the Jews who are oppressed in the Crimea, in Poland; he wants the Jews even from China and Constantinople—the black, the white and the yellow Jews—he wants them all to come to Ararat. He is going to build a kind of Palestine, a homeland for the Jews."

"But where is Ararat?" asked Abraham quite excited.

"Say, I believe you could understand this. Listen and I'll read it to you. Mr. Noah's secretary writes in her column:

From the *National Advocate*

An interesting conversation took place at our office yesterday between Mr. Leggett and Mr. Noah. It is a pleasure to report this to our readers.

Mr. Noah began by asking, "Mr. Leggett, have you heard that the government is parcelling out farm land on Grand Island in the Niagara River?"

"Yes, indeed," replied Mr. Leggett. "However, I am not especially interested."

"Nevertheless, you will buy 2500 acres of that land," Mr. Noah said, as he humorously pointed his forefinger at Mr. Leggett.

Those who are acquainted with Mr. Noah know that he is large and heavy. When he speaks, you simply have to listen to him. And when he shakes his finger at you, you just have to do anything he asks.

Without waiting for an answer Mr. Noah continued, "The land is full of timber and also makes good hunting and fishing ground."

Mr. Leggett caught the idea. As if thinking aloud he said, "The Erie

From the *National Advocate* (Continued)

Canal too will soon be completed. That will run from Buffalo to Albany. It will connect the Great Lakes with the Hudson River and so with the Atlantic Ocean. That will open commerce between this country and Europe. That's good. The charge for transportation will be much less. I will probably get Yates and McIntyre to buy some of that land too."

"Good," Noah said, as he vigorously shook Mr. Leggett's hand. "I know you have a good eye for business, and that you are a good Christian too. But there is more to this matter. I don't mind telling you I've decided to make a new home for my people; make them proud of being Jews. Like Noah of old I will begin a new world on Grand Island, and we must all buy land for this purpose."

Mr. Leggett shook hands and left with a promise to help.

This is the beginning of the City of Ararat. May it prosper!

"Abraham, are you asleep?" Judah asked.

"No, indeedy," came the quick reply.

"Now, then, explain what I read to you."

"Mr. Noah is having a dream—he wants to gather the sick, tired, oppressed Jews in the world and bring them to Grand Island across the Niagara. In that place all will be peaceful. He calls the place Ararat because they will find rest there."

Judah had not known that his little brother would understand so much.

"It is a grand idea to build a home for all those homeless Jews." He was talking to Abraham as if he were an adult. "I do so hope Mr. Noah will succeed in getting all the help he needs. Just now it's only a dream—just a dream—as you said."

Judah smiled as he began to do his homework.

*   *   *

The knocker on the door sounded, and Abraham's heart thumped. He ran quickly to get the evening paper which was delivered at the door. Abraham wanted to be first to read the news. He wanted to show Judah that he *could* understand "news"—especially if there was a picture in it. He hopefully opened the paper. Yes, there it was! Another picture. But there were no people in it, no ark and no animals. It looked like a brick with a sign on it. He read the words. Abraham was proud that he could read even the Hebrew.

SH'MA YISROEL ADONOY ELOHENU ADONOY ECHOD

ARARAT

A City of Refuge for the Jews

FOUNDED BY MORDECAI MANUEL NOAH, IN THE MONTH OF (TISHRI) SEPT. 1825—IN THE 50TH YEAR OF AMERICAN INDEPENDENCE.

Underneath the picture Abraham read, "Above is a picture of the cornerstone for the city of Ararat, which will be founded by Mr. Noah. The cornerstone ceremony will take place on Grand Island, where the stone will be laid, on September 2nd."

Abraham read and wondered, "So it's a stone! But why must they have a ceremony when they put only one stone down in a corner? That is funny!"

But the Children's Page was still funnier, and Abraham stretched himself comfortably on the floor to read it.

Soon Mr. Seixas, Abraham's father, came home with Judah for dinner. Judah turned to Abraham and asked, "Well, Abraham, did you hear any more about the 'Ararat Dream?' "

"Oh, sure," answered Abraham, trying to look wise, "they are going to put a stone down in a corner, and they will have a celebration."

But turning to his father, Abraham asked wonderingly: "Father, why do they need a celebration just to place one stone in a corner?"

Abraham's parents smiled as Judah began to laugh, holding his sides and repeating: "When they place one stone in a corner —that's a funny one. Ha! Ha! When they place one stone in a corner."

"I think that's a very good question," Mr. Seixas replied, "and you needn't laugh, Judah. This stone which they place somewhere on the ground is a sign. It's usually a sign that they hope to build a whole house or, as in this case, a whole city. The stone stands for a good beginning. Would you like to go with me to Grand Island to see the laying of that cornerstone?"

"Oh, would I? All the way from New York to Buffalo! What a trip!" Abraham cried, turning a somersault for joy.

"Just because Abraham asks silly questions, he'll go to Grand Island," Judah complained. "I know more about Grand Island than he does."

"You probably know more about it than Mr. Noah does," Mr. Seixas smiled kindly. "I'm afraid Mr. Noah has never even seen the land. But I did promise to go up with him, and I shall take the entire family with me, because I think it is going to be a memorable event."

The next three days were the longest in the calendar for Judah and Abraham. Every night Mr. Seixas told them about something that Mr. Noah was taking along to Grand Island: the corner stone, medals, silken garments. Mr. Noah kept packing bundle upon bundle into the coach. It seemed there would be much to hear and to see. Judah and Abraham were filled with excitement and expectation. At last they started out!

When they came to a little muddy village with unpaved streets, they were told they had reached Buffalo, which was the biggest city near Grand Island. Squirrels were scampering up and down the tall trees. They walked past a long row of frame cottages and log cabins. At last they stopped at Mr. Smith's house. Mr. Smith was the only one whom Mr. Noah knew in Buffalo.

"Well, there are great doings in Buffalo these days," Mr. Smith said proudly as he greeted them. "Hundreds of people have come to see the laying of the cornerstone. But I wonder how we are going to get them across to Grand Island."

Abraham and Judah opened their eyes wide. They began to fear the worst. "Won't they lay the cornerstone on Grand Island? Will Ararat remain a dream after all?" Abraham thought.

"There surely won't be enough boats to take all the people

across," Mr. Smith continued. "However, the pastor of the Episcopal Church has offered the church for the ceremony."

"Good," said Mr. Noah joyfully, "that shows a real brotherly feeling—to offer a Christian church in which to celebrate the laying of a cornerstone for a Jewish city of refuge!"

Abraham and Judah were disappointed. They had hoped to see Grand Island, and perhaps even some of the Indians there.

But all was forgotten when the next day they were awakened by a salute fired in front of the court house and the terrace facing the lake.

"Quick, Judah, get up! We had better get dressed right now or we may miss something." Abraham, full of excitement, shook his brother.

But Judah mumbled, "What time is it?"

"Five o'clock," whispered Abraham.

"Aw, go to sleep," replied his brother, "nothing's going to happen before 10 o'clock."

But Mr. and Mrs. Seixas were soon stirring. There were many things to be arranged, and by eight o'clock the Seixas family was at the church. They found it filled with people, many of whom had been there since before dawn. Troops guarded the church. At last the bugle sounded and the band began to play. Mordecai Manuel Noah ascended the platform.

"Look! See that beautiful red silk and that white fur? Now what do they call that?" Abraham nudged Judah.

"I see. Yes, it's beautiful. But it doesn't matter. There are more important things to see today."

At the church door the troops parted, one half going to the right and the other half to the left. The procession passed into the crowded church as the band played the grand march from *Judas Maccabeus*. Then the organ played "The Jubilate." And what was that on the table in the church? Abraham recognized it. It was that stone, the exact copy of which he had seen in the newspaper!

Abraham became restless during the service. But when Mordecai Manuel Noah arose, tall and stately, Abraham sat up with renewed interest.

"Look at those medals hanging from his neck!"

Mr. Noah straightened his high-peaked collar and the frills on his shirt.

"Oh, I do wish he would stop fussing and make his speech," Abraham whispered impatiently.

At last Mordecai Manuel Noah, the "new judge" in Israel began to speak:

"Whereas the time for peace on earth and good-will to man seems to be near, therefore I, Mordecai Manuel Noah, citizen of the U. S. A., Consul of Tunis, High Sheriff of New York, and by the grace of God Governor and judge of Israel, have issued this, my proclamation . . ."

"Who made him ruler?" Judah heard an old man mumble.

TODROS
GELLER

Noah continued, "announcing that a place of refuge will be built."

"He really thinks he is Noah building a new world again!" grumbled another man.

Mr. Noah continued, undisturbed. "Here in this city of Ararat, the Jews will live in peace."

"Oh how I should love to go up to Grand Island and plant the flag of Israel in the city of Ararat," said Abraham.

"The flag hasn't been made yet, Abraham," his father whispered. "When it is ready you will go."

"I'm getting tired," Abraham yawned.

But Mr. Noah continued: "In God's name, I revive, renew, and re-establish the government of the people under the protection of the United States of America. . . . Here we shall welcome the black Jews of India and Africa and our brothers from China."

"Ha-ha," laughed one of the men.

By now Judah and Abraham would have liked to leap upon this man who kept interrupting.

"A tax of 3 shekels yearly shall be collected from every Jew."

The man who had laughed, shouted, "Ha-ha, that's just a business."

But Noah continued as if he had heard nothing. Maybe he did hear nothing but his own proclamation!

Noah read the last line, "Given under our hand and seal in

the State of New York on the 2nd of Ab, 5586, in the 50th year of American independence."

Mr. Noah sat down amid a storm of applause. It looked as if the ceremony was over.

"What will happen now?" asked Abraham, impatiently.

"What will happen now?" Judah repeated after him, imitating his tone. "Hasn't enough happened yet? Now the procession will file out of the church. Then there will be a discharge of 24 guns to round out the great day for Ararat City. Mr. Noah will report the affair to the Buffalo *Patriot*."

"But I didn't mean that! I mean, what will happen about Ararat?" Abraham insisted. "If it isn't to remain a dream, when will they begin to build it?"

Abraham, not getting a satisfactory reply from Judah, turned to his father and urged, "Couldn't we go to Ararat—I mean Grand Island, at once?"

"But no one has gone there yet," his father said patiently. "The city must be built up first."

"Built up first?" Abraham repeated in surprise. "Aren't we American pioneers? I like to do my own building. I'd like to go and help build it."

"But how can we go? I'm so busy preaching in New York."

"But what about Mr. Noah," Judah asked. "Isn't he going to really build his Ararat?"

"He, too, is a very busy man—a playwright, a sheriff, a governor."

"Then who will build Ararat?" Abraham persisted.

"Maybe you will," his father said kindly, as they mounted the coach.

But Ararat, or Grand Island, was never built up. It remained a dream. You shall hear of others who also had great dreams. But they worked hard and even gave their lives that their dreams might come true.

The Fight Is On

BOHEMIA. . . .

"There goes one snowball! And it hit the mark, too," cried a freckled fellow, who seemed to be the leader of the gang.

And what a gang it was—about twenty or thirty boys! They had worked busily all afternoon making snowballs. They were getting ready for a real bombardment. The snowballs, hard and solid, were carefully placed in a basket. Now they were set!

But where were those Jew-boys? Didn't they always come at this hour to take extra Latin lessons from the Catholic priest?

The gang's fears were needless. Soon Isaac Mayer and his Jewish friends came along.

"Well, we won't need to worry about that gang today," David was saying. "It's too cold for them to be out."

"If I were not so eager to understand my Latin lesson a little better, I shouldn't have come either, in this bitter cold."

Isaac Mayer had hardly finished his sentence when bing,

bang; along came one snowball, a second, a third and a fourth. Isaac lost count. So did the Bohemian boys who were throwing them. The attack had begun in earnest. The unequal fight was on!

Before long the three Jewish boys were stretched on the ground. Isaac Mayer had fainted. With great difficulty the other two boys dragged themselves to their feet and lifted Isaac Mayer. Carrying him between them they reached the priest's house. The priest rubbed Isaac's hands and feet until finally Isaac came to.

As he opened his eyes he moaned: "Why must I be a Jew?"

The priest laid his hand soothingly on Isaac's head and said sadly: "To civilize those barbarians—to civilize those barbarians, my son."

Still somewhat dizzy, Isaac repeated, "I must civilize those barbarians." And Isaac never forgot those words.

*   *   *

New York. . . .

What a rush! and what a clamor! What hurrying and scurrying! Milkmen, rag pickers, fish-mongers, newsboys, pop corn vendors! What rumbling of wagons! What ear-splitting noises!

"How different from the beautiful town in Bohemia," Rabbi Isaac Mayer thought when he first wandered along the streets of New York with his family after 63 days on the ocean.

"What hustle and bustle! But this is America, the land of Freedom and Liberty. Here no one will call me names or throw snowballs at me until I faint. Here the government protects all its citizens, Jews and Gentiles alike. Here I shall have a chance to do the things I want to do. These thoughts gave Isaac Mayer new courage.

Rabbi Isaac Mayer and his family moved into a house on Browne Street. One evening his brother-in-law and a few acquaintances came to talk over with Isaac Mayer what he should do to earn his living in the United States.

One man by the name of Stein said, "This is how I see it. The Jews who have *good* minds stay in Europe. Those who come here must have *strong muscles*. You, too, Isaac Mayer, will have to fill a basket with wares and go peddling. The people here have no use for rabbis. Money is all that counts. Ideas, understanding, that's nothing. Take my advice, don't try to be a rabbi here. There is no one to listen to your teaching!"

"But don't they have synagogues here? If the people don't care about such things why do they support synagogues?" Rabbi Isaac Mayer asked.

"Oh well, they do that because they like to be presidents and give orders. Poor peddlers! Whom could they order about otherwise? But they don't have any real interest."

"I don't believe that," Isaac Mayer insisted. "The spirit is there, burning low, and I will fan it into a flame. I will fight the barbarians among the Jews as well as among the Gentiles."

Mr. Stein smiled at the burning energy and the great courage of the young rabbi.

Another man there said, "Don't bother with the Jews at all. Just sprinkle yourself with a few drops of water and become a Christian. Then every opportunity will be open to you."

"Become a Christian!" Isaac Mayer cried bitterly. "Is it for that that I left Bohemia? No, no! It's the mission of the Jew to teach the people around him that the Lord is one, and that the Ten Commandments must be obeyed by everybody. And where can it be done better than in this country—this country which based its Constitution on the laws of Moses and the teachings of the Prophets; this country where everybody is free! I have been sent here to teach the people."

"But you have a wife and child! You need food, clothing and a house to live in. And your preaching will not get you that," his brother-in-law, Mr. Bloch, remarked kindly. "Perhaps it will be a good thing for you to open a night school for the teaching of English. Many will be interested in that!"

Isaac Mayer listened politely and smiled. He had already made up his mind.

* * *

The next day, Rabbi Isaac Mayer Wise went to see Dr. Max Lilienthal. He had a letter of introduction from a friend in Germany. As Isaac Mayer was walking along the street he noticed a man with an old straw hat pulled down half way over his eyes. He was dressed in a dirty linen coat and wore a pair of gold-rimmed spectacles. On his shoulders he carried a

TODROS
GELLER

large, heavy basket, and he was dragging himself along with a great deal of effort. He was looking about anxiously and searchingly.

"Have you lost anything?" Rabbi Wise asked. "I've lost —I've lost everything!" he cried. "I have lost my English language."

"You have lost your English language!—I do not understand," said the Rabbi, a little worried.

"Neither do I—and that's the trouble. When I arrived in New York they said to me: Loeb, you must buy a basket of pins, needles, ribbons and shoe laces—'kudel mudel' we call it, then you must go peddling in the country. I cried, 'The country speaks English, and I do not. How in the world can I get along?' 'That makes no difference!' they told me, 'We will write everything down for you.' Well, they gave me the basket of 'kudel mudel' and wrote down the English language on a piece of paper for me. Now I have lost the English language, and I am helpless."

Though Rabbi Wise had many things to attend to, he said to the peddler, "I can help you with the English language. You write the names of the things in German and I will tell you the English." So the peddler found the English language. He was happy again.

Rabbi Isaac Mayer then hurried on to Dr. Lilienthal's house. He was most cordially received. Rabbi Lilienthal promised Dr. Wise that he would do all in his power to help him.

When Isaac Mayer came home he told his wife the story of the peddler, and she said: "Oh, Isaac, you always aim high. Here you find a nation of peddlers and you want to turn them into a nation of priests."

"Yes, I shall turn them into priests. Only, in order to do that, I must teach them the Bible and in Hebrew, at that. When they learn that, they will be their own priests."

*   *   *

"Do you see this notice," Isaac Mayer asked his wife as he handed her the paper. Mrs. Wise took *The Argus* and read:

"Rabbi Cohen of Jerusalem, who is a member of the Society for The Improvement of the Condition of the Jews, will speak this evening in Dr. Wyckoff's church. The lower floor will be reserved for the clergy, church officers and their leaders. The general public will have seats in the gallery."

Mrs. Wise laid down the paper: "What does that mean?"

"That means that the craze for turning Jews into Christians is even greater here than it is in Bohemia. The only difference is that here they can't harm the Jews because the government protects them. So now they have found another way. They say they are taking pity on the 'poor Jews.' They will give them food and clothing for a small price. All they need do is turn Christian. They don't have to pay any money."

The Rabbi was so excited that he had to mop his forehead with his handkerchief.

"But Isaac dear, what can you do about it?" Mrs. Wise pleaded.

"Give me my frock-coat and a white neckerchief, too. Here is where I'll put my knowledge of English to use!"

Mrs. Wise went to the clothes closet immediately and began to do as she had been told, almost tearfully repeating, "But what can you do about it?"

"So they are taking pity on us Jews! Is that it?" Isaac muttered as he buttoned up his coat. "They are worried for our souls, are they? Well, I'll remove their worries!" Isaac almost screamed at his frightened wife. "Goodbye, dear, I'm going to Dr. Wyckoff's meeting!"

Mrs. Wise held her hands to her head and pleaded, "Isaac, have pity on your family. They'll stone you. You won't have a friend left, Jew or Gentile!"

But Isaac had already closed the door behind him. Isaac Mayer stopped to call for two Gentile friends (Unitarians) and was soon at the door of the church.

The door-keeper stopped Isaac Mayer and asked, "Are you a Protestant Clergyman?"

"I am a clergyman who *protests* against what you are doing. Therefore I am a *'protestant'* clergyman."

The doorman was so frightened that without another word he let Isaac Mayer in.

Fearlessly Isaac Mayer walked clear to the front of the church and sat down close to the pulpit.

Soon a dark, well-fed man, with small black eyes and a very large nose, walked in.

"That," thought Isaac Mayer, "must be the famous missionary, Cohen."

Dr. Wyckoff, who was the chairman, arose and spoke of the poor unfortunate Jews, whose souls must be saved. Then he asked, "Does anyone wish to say anything on the subject?" In this way he hoped to introduce the missionary.

But before he could say another word, Rabbi Wise rose and said, "May I have the floor please, Mr. Chairman?"

Dr. Wyckoff was astonished. He began to hem and haw but Isaac Mayer didn't wait for his decision. He began to speak:

"I am one of those Jews about whom you speak. We don't need your make-believe charity. We ourselves take care of our poor, the widows, and the orphans. The Jews will not be converted to Christianity by gold or anything else. I move that this meeting be adjourned."

One of his Unitarian friends seconded the motion. Wyckoff had to put the motion to a vote.

"All those in favor of adjournment will say 'aye.'"

A rousing "aye" thundered from the gallery. "All those opposed, 'No.'"

Only a few women had the courage to say no. The meeting was adjourned. For a long time no such meeting was called again in that city.

*　　*　　*

"Mother, please don't forget to wake me up early tomorrow. We're going to have a rehearsal of the choir."

"The choir?" Mrs. Friedman repeated questioningly as she looked up from her sewing. "What choir?"

"Haven't you heard about all that Rabbi Wise has done! Two months ago nobody paid any attention to him. And now he is changing Judaism in America. Yes, mother, we have a choir, and we shall all be ready to sing during the Passover services.

"It was a very difficult thing to do, because in the entire congregation there were only two Jewish grown-ups who could sing. They were bassos. But Rabbi Wise wasn't discouraged. Not he—he went ahead and engaged a music teacher for us children in the school. And girls were admitted to the choir, too. Not only that," Sarah paused a moment to catch her breath, "but by Yom Kippur we shall have an organ, too. And there will be beautiful music in the synagogue, such as they must have had in the Temple in Jerusalem."

"Oh, mother," Sarah interrupted herself, throwing her arms around her mother's neck, "why don't you join Rabbi Wise's synagogue? Those Saturday morning services at our synagogue are so long!"

Mrs. Friedman spoke quietly. "Yes, I suppose the prayers are long, as you say. But I go to the synagogue to talk to my Lord. I want to tell him of my troubles and my joys. Those prayers which you think long, say it all for me."

"But mother, why?" Sarah was about to ask, but her mother was gazing off into the distance, with smiling, dreamy eyes. Then she said:

"We Orthodox Jews go to the synagogue daily, three times a day. For us it is almost our home. In the synagogue we study, in the synagogue we have celebrations, in the synagogue we cry to the Lord for help. The synagogue is our home. Do we wear stiff shirts and walk on tiptoe at home? No. And we don't feel that we have to do those things in the synagogue either. We Orthodox Jews *live* in it. We don't expect this Dr. Wise to think as we do, but we certainly won't join him!"

"Mother," Sarah said gently, "I still say you are missing a lot! Now I love to go to the services, because there is beautiful music and an interesting sermon, and in English at that! Besides the women do not have to sit behind a railing like prisoners." Meanwhile Sarah was getting ready for bed. "It is so nice, Mother. Mr. and Mrs. Sproberg and their children all sit together. It's called a family pew."

"Yes," sighed Mrs. Friedman. "I suppose you young people will have to decide these things for yourselves. You have to live your own lives."

But Sarah had already fallen asleep. She dreamed that she heard the beautiful strains of the organ and the voices of the choir as they sang a hymn from Sulzer.

She saw Rabbi Wise standing in the pulpit, determined to fight Orthodoxy, Christian and Jewish alike.

"We will bring beauty into the lives of our children," the Rabbi was saying. "They won't have to go to Palestine to build a beautiful homeland. They will live beautifully right here in America. We shall teach them how to make the Law of Moses, the law of brotherhood and good will, the law of the whole world!"

"If only we could all sit together in a family pew!" Mrs. Friedman heard Sarah murmur in her sleep.

* * *

On Saturday, Sarah hurried to the synagogue as usual. As she sat down, she heard someone whisper: "I wonder whether the Rabbi will preach today. I heard his cap and gown were stolen."

Everyone seemed restless. A storm was brewing. When would it break?

At the usual time, however, Rabbi Wise, dressed in his ordinary street-clothes, arose and began to preach.

"To you, young people, I say, do not worry about what kind of food you eat. There is only one rule. Do not eat that which is unhealthy. Judaism concerns itself with the kind of lives you live, and not with the kind of food you eat. Its teaching deals with your way of life and not with your stomach. What you need is trained men who will teach you how to live a Jewish life, men who will help you to understand the teachings of the Bible."

But the people of his congregation were not listening as

attentively as they usually did. "Who dared to play that trick on the rabbi?" they kept wondering.

One of the choir members said, "Let us get him a new outfit for next week, and keep it under lock and key until the rabbi puts it on."

Before the week was over the cap and gown lay safely locked away in the synagogue. On Saturday the synagogue was crowded. Everybody was eager to see what would happen. The young people were happy to see their rabbi dressed in his usual rabbinical cap and gown. They sang beautifully through the first part of the service.

When the choir had finished its hymn and Rabbi Wise was about to step up to the pulpit, the beadle gave him a note, signed by the president of the congregation.

It read: "You are hereby notified that you are not to preach today."

Rabbi Wise paid no attention to the note and began to speak:

"Last week we were discussing leadership in American Judaism. But I tell you that we must do more than build a college for the training of rabbis; we must form a union of all the Hebrew Congregations in America. Only in that way——"

And just then the president of the congregation stepped up to him and muttered, "I tell you, you shall not preach today!"

But the Rabbi only raised his voice as he finished his sentence, "Only by a union of all American Hebrew Congregations shall we be able to accomplish the God-given task of building American Judaism."

"A college, a union—Shtuss! Nonsense!" exclaimed one old man. "We won't stand for this!"

The president, without saying another word, suddenly struck the cap from the rabbi's head.

What an uproar followed! It was as if the synagogue had caught fire. Sarah and her friends ran down the stairs leading from the gallery. They wanted to protect their rabbi. But in a moment a constable had appeared.

"You will have to come with me, Rabbi," he said. "Sorry, but we can't have any trouble-makers here!"

And Rabbi Wise was led through the streets. Some of the members and all the young people followed him.

"What a disgrace! What a shame!" cried one of them. "How ridiculous to say that Rabbi Wise is a trouble-maker!"

As the Rabbi was walking along he thought of his childhood and youth in Bohemia. "Hard work teaching the barbarians! But I will *not* give up!"

When Rabbi Wise was brought before the court his case was dismissed for lack of evidence.

The Rabbi conducted New Year's services in his own home. The choir sat in the hall and those members of his congregation who believed in him sat in the two parlors.

"Be brave and of good courage. He who wants to do great things must be ready to receive hard knocks," the rabbi said.

Dr. Joseph Lewi, a member, arose and said: "Dr. Wise, you are the bearer of a new idea in American Judaism, and we are ready to stand by you to the end."

* * *

Rabbi Wise continued his good work. He was enthusiastic and full of energy.

"Wc shall continue our work. We shall publish this paper, *The Israelite*. It will be like a shining light to American Jewry."

"How will you do it?" his brother-in-law, Bloch, asked.

"How?" Rabbi Wise repeated, as a faint smile played about his lips. "We shall buy presses and set up a print-shop."

"Ach so!" Bloch began, "we shall buy presses, and with what, pray?"

"Now you have asked a fair question," Rabbi Wise smiled. "We can get six month's credit! And we shall establish the firm of Bloch and Company."

On August 10th, 1855, the following call appeared in *The Israelite*.

THE FIRST CONFERENCE

In the name of Israel's God and Israel's religion, the ministers and delegates of the Israelitish Congregations are respectfully requested to assemble in a conference to take place in Cleveland, Ohio.

By order of the American Rabbis

All rabbis, Orthodox and Reform, signed!

October 17, 1855! Another dream come true! The First Conference of the United Jewish Congregations of America met in Cleveland, and Rabbi Wise was elected the first president.

Slowly and painfully Rabbi Wise was teaching his people. He had to fight at every step. But American Judaism was becoming free, united and respected.

Of Thee I Sing

"Heigh-ho, heigh-ho,
As down the hill we go!"

A merry throng of boys and girls were sledding. As they swooped down the steep hill, their spirited song rang out, "Heigh-ho, heigh-ho." Their cheeks were red. Their eyes were sparkling. The sun was shining brightly. The whole world seemed full of fun. They picked up their sleds and trudged back up the hill. Some slid back and had to be dragged up the hill by their merry, teasing friends.

Suddenly, one of the girls cried, "Oh, look who is here, 'tearful Emma' herself!"

"Stop that," warned one of the older girls. "Her name is Emma Lazarus, and she is a very nice girl."

"Nice, but—just call her over and you'll find out."

One of the girls called: "Emma, Emma, come on up to the top of the hill."

Emma was a pale little girl of eleven, with an oval face and olive skin. She seemed frightened, and hesitated.

"Come on, Emma. Be a sport this once. It's really lots of fun!"

Emma, with a girl pulling her at either side, at last reached the top.

"Have a seat," one of the girls pointed to a sled.

"Thank you, but I can't stand all this noise. I'll join that group. They don't seem to be so noisy. See, they are making a snowman. That's not so rough."

The girls smiled to one another, whispering, "We're too rough." They followed Emma just to see what she would do.

The sun shone on the dazzling white snow. Emma suddenly stooped, gathered up some freshly fallen snow and began to roll and shape it.

"Do you want any help?" one of the girls asked.

Instead of replying Emma asked, "Did you ever read the Greek myths? Many of them are sad, sad stories. That's why I like them."

The girls whispered to one another, " 'Sad, sad,' that's 'tearful Emma,' all right."

Emma, without noticing their remarks, continued: "I have just written a poem about a Greek goddess. Her name was Daphne. Now I shall try to make the figure of Daphne."

"Oh, Daphne," the girls repeated without understanding.

"Yes, 'Daphne, the fair one, with the sea-blue eyes.' "

And Emma began to recite a poem which she had written about Daphne. The children did not understand the poem. They laughed at Emma as they repeated the first line after her: "Daphne, the fair one, with the sea-blue eyes."

"Here's a blue button for her eyes," said one of the girls, as she handed Emma a button, with mock helpfulness.

"Oh, that's fine!" exclaimed Emma. She had no idea that the girls were laughing at her.

Emma, who was still busy making the snow figure, sighed, saying, "Daphne was turned into a laurel tree. Do you think I could shape the snow into leaves?"

"And then hang them on to the bark?" The girl laughed.

"No. I'm afraid not," one of the nicer girls answered. "You had better go home, Emma, and work with clay."

"I guess you're right," answered Emma seriously. "But I shall try to make a Venus of Milo, another Greek goddess. It will be easy to make her, because she has no arms."

"No arms, no arms!" The girls again laughed, whispering and nudging one another.

Suddenly Emma rose from the ground, saying, "I'm going home. There is no fun in working with the snow. I'd rather write poems."

Without another word, Emma rushed down the hill. She was soon at home. Her mother, hearing her enter, called:

"Emma, dear, why did you come back so soon? Why don't you stay out and get some fresh air and sunshine?"

To which Emma replied:

> One by one, the summer flowers
> Now are dying.
> She, the fairest of them all, is
> With them lying.

"That's the beginning of a new poem I'm writing. That's for my friend who just died. I think I'll call it 'In Memoriam.'"

Emma's mother sighed. "She is certainly an unusual child! I wonder what sort of person she'll grow up to be."

To Emma she said: "Won't you stop reading those Greek stories? Won't you ever stop thinking of your dead friend?"

By way of answer, Emma sat down on the piano-stool and began to play a funeral march, her eyes filling with tears as she played.

"What is going to become of this child?" her mother wondered, as she brought in a glass of milk for Emma.

The years passed; Emma was no longer a child.

One morning her sister came running in with the announcement, "Emma, here are your poems, 'Afternoon' and 'Evening' printed in Lippincott's magazine, and 'June Night' and 'August Moon' are in the Century magazine!"

Emma smiled quietly, without even bothering to look at the magazine. Nothing seemed to make Emma happy.

"Besides," continued her sister, "here's a letter for you. Look whose name is on the back of the envelope. It's the great Russian writer, Turgenef!"

"Please open it and read it to us!" Her sisters gathered around Emma and coaxed her. "Do read it to us!"

Emma opened the letter and began, "I have read your book, *Alide,* with the liveliest interest . . ."

Suddenly there was a cry from newsboys outside: "Extra, Extra—Riots, Murder, Extra, Extra!"

Emma stopped reading. All three listened to the newsboy. "Property destroyed! One hundred thousand made homeless! Extra, Extra!"

"Paper-boy, paper-boy," called Emma through the window. In a moment she was reading the news.

"It's terrible! It's unbelievable! Bloody riots! Pogroms! Blood accusations! Again they are accusing the Jews in Russia of killing Christian children in order to use their blood at the Seder ceremony. And the Jews who have now settled on farms or in larger cities must go back to the 'Pale' in Poland and Lithuania, to those towns in which the Jews are allowed to live." Emma's eyes began to glow; her cheeks were flaming. Her deep black eyes looked into the distance.

"I hear the call. Yes, it's the trumpet call for me! What have I been doing all these years? What have I been writing about? About Greek myths, about the Christianity of the Middle Ages, about the musician Schumann. These things are not nearly so close to me as my own people. Give me some paper. Quick!"

Both of Emma's sisters hurried to her side with pen and paper. Emma sat down and wrote:

Wake, Israel, wake!
Recall today the . . . Maccabean rage . . .
Oh for Jerusalem's trumpet now
To blow a blast of shattering power,
To wake the sleepers high and low
And arouse them to the urgent hour! . . .
Let but an Ezra rise anew
To lift the Banner of the Jew!

Emma was writing a new kind of poetry. She was writing about her people, the Jews.

"Emma, dear," her older sister reminded her gently, "It's time for lunch." But Emma paid no attention. She continued to write.

She wrote another poem, called "The Crowing of the Red Cock," which ends:

"Coward? Not he who faces death,
Who singly against worlds has fought."

At last, toward evening her sister forced Emma to stop writing and take some food. She did, and then hurried to get her hat and coat.

How different from the child of fourteen years ago! What energy! What enthusiasm!

"Come with me, Leona. I am going over to the Heilprins. I must do something for these thousands of unfortunate Jews who will be fleeing to our American shores. I love America! I am proud that *my* country, America, will help *my* people!"

They were soon at Dr. Michael Heilprin's house.

"Dr. Heilprin," Emma said, as she pointed to herself, "You have here a Jewess returned to the fold. I have been dead till now, but now I am beginning to live. Say not I was born in July, 1849. Say rather I was born in March, 1882." Emma spoke with energy and fire.

"And began to write and work immediately. Quite a genius!" replied Dr. Heilprin smiling. "Well, then, what shall we teach this infant?"

"Hebrew, first of all. I want to know the language of the Bible; then Jewish literature and Jewish history."

And Emma Lazarus learned quickly. She now began to write poems on Jewish subjects—the Jewish New Year, and the Feast of Lights. She translated the great poems of Ibn Gabirol and Jehudah Halevi.

*   *   *

America, 1882.

They came with bag and baggage. Pale, hollow-eyed, bent with suffering and fear. Old Jews from Russia with long white beards. Young Jews who looked as if they had not slept for weeks. They came—the women with wigs covering their hair, or heads covered with kerchiefs. But there were strong, healthy young men and women among them, too.

Emma Lazarus went to Ward's Island, the refuge which

awaited them all. There was a smile on her face and joy in her heart as she received her people. She was happy that she could be of use to them.

Emma Lazarus greeted the immigrants. She could speak neither Yiddish nor Russian, and so she had brought an interpreter. She found out about the lives and interests of these people.

Emma's secretary asked, "Miss Lazarus, where shall we place this group?"

"They will go to the National Farm School near Philadelphia."

"And the other group?"

"They will join the trade schools of Baron de Hirsch. And that third group will have to go to the Chicago committee."

Dr. Heilprin came in and smiled encouragingly, "With your help, Miss Lazarus, I am sure we shall do much for our unfortunate brethren."

"I hope so. I know we shall help them find a way to earn their living. But will that help the Jewish people as a *whole?*"

Dr. Heilprin looked at his pupil fondly, "As long as we have poets like you, we need not worry."

Emma was at last returning home from Ward's Island. She had been working very hard for weeks. Yet, when she reached home she could not sleep. She sat in bed and wrote:

"It is well that we organize for the relief of oppressed Jews. But that is not enough. We must have a national center, a national homeland in Palestine. We must work to build up this idea of a homeland for the Jews in Palestine."

And far into the night Emma Lazarus wrote her "Epistles to the Hebrews."

A few years passed. They were happy years, for Emma Lazarus was working for her people, the Jews. But her health was poor. She went several times to Europe, hoping to improve.

While in Europe she would say to her European friends, "It's America that has given freedom to the Jewish people. It's America that has given freedom to the negroes."

In 1886 when France presented the Statue of Liberty to America, Emma Lazarus returned to her beloved country in order that she might be present at the ceremony.

Emma, now a noted American Jewish poetess, was invited to write a poem for the celebration. She called it "The New Colossus."

The day for the presentation arrived. Many had gathered on the Island where the statue was to be placed. Emma Lazarus, pale and weary, dragged herself to the pedestal of the statue and there read her poem with a voice that shook with feeling:

THE NEW COLOSSUS

Here at our sea-washed, sunset gates shall stand
A mighty woman with a torch; whose flame
Is the imprisoned lightning—and her name—Mother
    of Exiles,

TODROS
GELLER

"Keep, ancient lands, your storied pomp!" cries she
With silent lips, "Give me your tired, your poor,
Your huddled masses yearning to be free.

"Send these, the homeless . . . to me;
I lift my lamp beside the golden door."

There was loud applause. Emma dropped into the chair which someone had placed near her.

A group of young women who had played in the snow with Emma twenty-five years before, wiped the tears from their eyes and said in hushed, respectful tones, "That's 'tearful Emma.' Isn't it terrible to think how we poked fun at her?"

"And do you know this poem she has read will be engraved inside the pedestal of the Statue of Liberty, and it will remain there as long as this torch of freedom will shine over our land?"

Then one of the women stepped up to the pedestal and presented Emma with a beautifully bound copy of her own poems on which the ladies had written: "To our never-to-be-forgotten 'Tearful Emma,' a noble American Jewish Poetess."

Emma had regained her energy. She arose and cried in a clear, happy voice, her eyes shining: "Come now, this is not a funeral, this is a happy occasion. Let's all sing——

"My country 'tis of Thee,
Sweet land of Liberty,
Of Thee I sing!"

Lost! A Hundred Dollars

"THINK of it! A hundred dollars!" said Mrs. Ben Jehudah, opening her big, dark eyes so wide that they shone like two glistening diamonds in their hollow sockets. "You know, Eliezer, it *is* hard to get along with those four dollars a month which you receive as assistant editor on that weekly. I am *not* complaining. But do go and claim that money they sent you from Russia."

Mrs. Ben Jehudah glanced sadly about the dark basement dwelling. It was damp and cold. Eliezer was coughing. His wife lay in bed, very sick.

"I'll go. I'll try to get that money, but I shall let them know that my name is Ben Jehudah, and not Jehudavitch, as they have it written here."

All this Eliezer said in Hebrew. Though he had studied in Germany, France and Russia and could speak well the language of those countries, Eliezer used *only* Hebrew.

He looked down lovingly at his wife and said, "I know, dear. It is hard. The children are not so well either. But, remember the condition? Remember in Lithuania, you agreed to get married, to come to live in Jerusalem and speak only Hebrew, even though you had never spoken a word of it before!"

While Eliezer was talking Mrs. Ben Jehudah lay on the pillow, hardly opening her eyes. But at these words she raised herself in the bed. Her eyes lit up again, and she spoke eagerly.

"Yes, I remember. I wanted nothing more than to go with you to our own land, Palestine, and there speak our own language! And here I am now, learning the language rather well. No?" she looked up smilingly at her husband. "But the child, Ittamar, he doesn't seem to be learning it so well."

Mrs. Ben Jehudah sank back on her pillow exhausted. That deep, hungry look came back to her eyes.

"Maybe if he were allowed to play with the other children and speak Yiddish, German, or whatever language they speak—maybe then he might learn more quickly. Yes, I agreed to speak Hebrew, but most of the words that we need for regular use even you don't know, Eliezer."

Just then, as if to prove Mrs. Ben Jehudah's point, Ittamar

came over to the bed and pointed to a dish of cereal on the table.

"Aani chafaitz bazeh" (I want that—that), he kept repeating.

Mrs. Ben Jehudah looked at her husband questioningly. She didn't know the Hebrew word for cereal. Eliezer hung his head and smiled. He, too, didn't know it offhand.

Ittamar, meanwhile, became impatient. He began to cry, "Give it to me, give it to me!"

"Dye-sa," said Eliezer quickly. "Ittamar wants 'dye-sa.' Here is the 'dye-sa.'" From his knowledge of Hebrew, Eliezer thought that that would be the right word to use.

Ittamar began to eat the cereal, as Eliezer rushed to his writing-table and wrote down the new word for cereal, *dye-sa*. He then looked in the Bible, the Talmud and the writings of the great Hebrew poets, to see whether the word had been used that way before. Sometimes he could not even find a word to use and had to make up his own words. So Eliezer began to prepare a modern Hebrew dictionary.

Mrs. Ben Jehudah turned and sighed, "It's very difficult. Can it be that Ittamar is deaf? Or maybe he just doesn't hear enough of the language to learn how to speak it." Mrs. Ben Jehudah's eyes filled with tears. "I don't know—Oh, I don't know," she kept repeating.

In order to encourage his wife and also to keep her from talking, because she was so weak—Ben Jehudah said, "If we, the young people, don't work for the rebuilding of our language, who will? You don't expect anything of the old Jews. They just come here to build graves, graves for themselves, the Jewish people and our language.

As Eliezer continued to work on the dictionary, Mrs. Ben Jehudah returned to the money question. "You, with that horrible cough; and the children certainly need better food!"

"Yes, I know. I will go to the post office and claim the hundred dollars they sent us."

Eliezer bent over the trunk and picked up a talis (a prayer shawl) and wrapped it about his shoulders as his ancestors had done for centuries before him.

Mrs. Ben Jehudah stared, wide-eyed. "Aren't you going to the post office?" she asked.

"Yes, that's why I'm getting dressed!"

"Dressed!" Mrs. Ben Jehudah repeated blankly, afraid to ask any more.

"Yes," Eliezer said forcefully, "just as I shall make Hebrew once more the language of the Jews, so shall I make the talis the national garb of our people."

Eliezer then turned to Ittamar and said (in Hebrew, of course) "Take care of Mother. Give her some water and some fruit, and be a good boy. I shall be back soon with a lot of money, and Ittamar will get a lot of new toys."

Mrs. Ben Jehudah smiled faintly as her husband left the house.

*   *   *

"There he goes, the mad-man! The destroyer of Israel! He calls himself Ben Jehudah! Who needs him here? Let him go back to the ship that brought him!" So spoke an old Jew heatedly. "I tell you," he continued, "Hebrew is a holy tongue, the language of the Bible."

"Of course," agreed his companion as they made their way through the narrow streets of Jerusalem. "Hebrew should be used only for special occasions, like births and marriages."

"Yes, and for prayers. But not every day, or for ordinary things! Who ever heard of using Hebrew in every-day speech!"

"We must do something about it, Mendel. You know he has opened a school to teach children. He wants to teach them Hebrew. Only Hebrew and *in* Hebrew! *That* should become their mother tongue! What an idea!"

Reuben pointed his forefinger accusingly at Mendel and said, "I tell you, that's just the kind of Jew who keeps the Messiah from coming. People like him spoil everything holy. Who can trust such a man with children?"

Ben Jehudah, meanwhile, had reached the post office. Breathlessly he went over to the window and showed the notice he had received, stating that one hundred dollars awaited him at the post office. The postmaster looked up at him, noticed the prayer shawl around his neck and wondered whether such a man could be trusted with a hundred dollars. Still, there was the note! If the man signed the name on the note, he, the post-master, had no right to withhold the money from him.

He handed Ben Jehudah a paper and said: "Please sign on the dotted line."

Ben Jehudah picked up the pen and wrote, "Eliezer Ben Jehudah." The postmaster compared his signature with that on the note.

"Are you Eliezer Jehudavitch?" the postmaster asked him.

"Yes, I am; only I write it in Hebrew."

All this Eliezer said, of course, in Hebrew. The postmaster did not understand him, but he got the idea from Ben Jehudah's gestures. By now the postmaster was convinced that he was dealing with a lunatic—but still he had to be polite.

"See this envelope?" the postmaster said, as he pointed to the address. "Just write *this* name, just as it is on the envelope."

"But my name is Ben Jehudah, and *that* is Jehudavitch."

"If you refuse to sign *this* name, I cannot give you the money."

Ben Jehudah refused to sign anything but his Hebrew name.

Pale as a ghost, and thin as a skeleton, Ben Jehudah threw the prayer shawl over him and started for home.

With the few pennies he had in his pocket, he stopped to buy some food for his family. Eliezer entered one of the stores and looked for some bread.

"Lechem, lechem," Eliezer said a number of times, until the storekeeper learned the word.

"Yes, I know, you want 'lechem,' but I still don't know what 'lechem' is," the storekeeper said impatiently.

Eliezer began to make chewing and swallowing movements. So the storekeeper offered him some cake.

"Lo, lo zot. Ein li dai kessef." (No, not that, I haven't enough money.)

Finally Ben Jehudah had to leave that store without buying, because the man could not understand him. Besides, Ben Jehudah wouldn't buy from anybody who did not speak Hebrew with him.

He entered another store and said, "B'vakashah, lechem." And he waited until the storekeeper answered, "Hineh lechem." He then asked for other things, but the storekeeper had to speak Hebrew to him each time. That was one of the ways in which Ben Jehudah taught the people Hebrew.

Today, however, Ben Jehudah could not spend much time in the stores. He wanted to hurry back to his sick wife. Sadly Ben Jehudah entered the cellar dwelling. As he opened the door, Ittamar stood near the bed holding his mother's hand.

"Sh—sh," he motioned his father. "Mamma is sleeping."

"Where are my new toys, Daddy?" Ittamar asked happily.

"I couldn't get them today. Some other time!" Ben Jehudah whispered as he gave him a slice of bread.

With a rapidly beating heart, Ben Jehudah went to the bedside and listened to his wife's breathing. As he bent over, she opened her eyes.

"Oh, Eliezer," she said, "you have the hundred dollars now. Good! Now you will be able to move out of this cellar!"

"Yes," Ben Jehudah answered, his lips barely moving.

"And you will marry my younger sister, and she will be a mother to our children."

"Yes," Eliezer answered, with tears rolling down his cheeks. "I promise."

*   *   *

It was a cold wintry day, much colder than one ever sees in Palestine. No sun was shining. The clouds were hanging low in the sky. There weren't many who came to the funeral of Mrs. Ben Jehudah. Wasn't she the wife of that wicked man, Ben Jehudah? Only a witch would have dared to marry him!

A few of her close neighbors had known the kindness and the heroism of Mrs. Ben Jehudah. Those came to shed a tear at her coffin. But no more. Only Ittamar and his father walked behind the coffin as the pall-bearers carried it toward the Mount of Olives for burial.

As they were leaving, some of the Jews complained that they did not want Ben Jehudah's wife on their burial ground.

Hearing this, Ben Jehudah took a spade and cried wildly: "I will dig her a grave right here, in her own garden, among her own flowers."

That, however, was not the Jewish way. Jews do not bury the dead among the living.

"After all, Mrs. Ben Jehudah was a Jewess even if she did marry Ben Jehudah. Poor woman!" they said, pityingly.

And so Mrs. Ben Jehudah, the first woman who went to Palestine to help make it a Jewish homeland, the first woman who agreed to speak Hebrew and nothing but Hebrew, was buried in the Land of the Hebrews.

*   *   *

It was not long after the death of Mrs. Ben Jehudah that two Turkish guards entered the house of Ben Jehudah and asked for Eliezer.

"I am he," Eliezer answered in Hebrew.

"You are under arrest for writing revolutionary articles. You are a traitor to the Turkish government. You are organizing schools, you lead clubs and you speak nothing but Hebrew; and you speak against the government. Come on."

Hemdah, Mrs. Ben Jehudah's sister, began to cry. It had all come so suddenly that Eliezer was bewildered. He really had nothing to say.

Turning to Hemdah he consoled her: "Don't cry. It won't be long. About a year, I guess. That isn't much. Besides, I shall put the time to good use there. Only, do come to visit me and bring Ittamar with you."

Ittamar had been at his grandfather's house for a few days. On his return Hemdah told him what had happened and they both started out for the prison.

After making their way through the narrow, winding streets of old Jerusalem, they reached the prison. A guard opened a heavy iron door and ushered them into a dirty, dingy little cell.

On the table a dim light shone in a broken lantern. Ben Jehudah, surrounded by many books, as many as the cell could hold, sat at the table reading. And he was writing in a big, thick note-book.

"Father," said Ittamar, "why are you working so hard, and why do you write in such a thick book?"

"I shall write down all the new words that you and your mother and your sister learned together. Then I shall make a *mill-on,* a wordbook—a dictionary of the Hebrew language. Then the Jewish people after us won't have as hard a time as we did."

"Oh!" Ittamar exclaimed admiringly, "if you can write such a big book, you must be a big man!"

Ben Jehudah lifted his son onto the table and said, "Now *you* are a big man; bigger than I."

"Yes," Ittamar answered, "only on the table, no place else."

Hemdah and Ittamar had to leave soon. Ben Jehudah continued to work on his dictionary.

*   *   *

A few years had passed. Ben Jehudah had come out of prison and was continuing his hard work, to make Hebrew a modern, living language. A number of schools were now teaching Hebrew *in* Hebrew. The clubs held meetings at which they spoke in Hebrew. The children spoke and sang Hebrew.

TODROS
GELLER

One day Hemdah, who had become Ben Jehudah's wife, and Ittamar, his son, pulled Ben Jehudah away from his work. Unwillingly Ben Jehudah followed them along the streets. Suddenly he stopped in front of a store. What did he see? A neon sign in Hebrew! It was hanging from the side of the store in which, a few years ago, Ben Jehudah had not been able to buy anything because the owner did not speak Hebrew. Lifting his eyes, Ben Jehudah saw that the whole block had neon signs in Hebrew.

Soon a band began to play. Parents, teachers and children were marching down the street. They were carrying banners and placards. On them were printed, "We Want Hebrew!" "Hebrew for Us," "Hebrew Is Our Language!"

They soon stopped marching. And the children's spokesman stood up on a barrel and began to talk in Hebrew: "We will not return to school unless Hebrew, and *not* German, is to be the language of our school, the new Polytechnic College."

"Yes, Hebrew!" went up the shout.

Ben Jehudah looked on and smiled, well pleased. He had suffered much, but the seed he had planted was taking root. His plant was even bearing fruit.

"If I Forget Thee..."

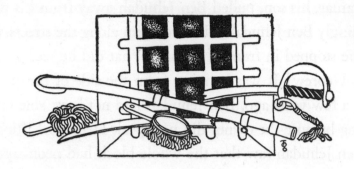

"DEATH to the traitor. Death is his just punishment!" So cried the mob as they filled the Champ de Mars in Paris. It was a cold, dreary day in January, 1894.

Alfred Dreyfus, a Jewish captain in the artillery, was being marched along the field between two guards.

In spite of the weather a merry crowd had gathered. They were dressed gayly. They laughed and shouted as if it were some great holiday. And it was a holiday for most of them. They were anti-Semites. They hated Jews. And today a Jew, Captain Dreyfus, was going to be put to shame. And why? While they were waiting for Captain Dreyfus to appear the mob was discussing "the affair," as it was called.

"Of course the Jew, Dreyfus, wrote that letter to the German War Office," exclaimed a Frenchman to his neighbor. "They say this Jew gave him a list of all the important secrets about the French army. That's why the letter is called the bordereau (a list). It's just like a Jew to betray our country!" Though it was

202

very cold, the man had to unbutton his coat. The mere thought of the "Jewish traitor" made him burn with excitement.

A young man who was blowing into his palms to keep them warm, said timidly:

"I am sorry to disagree with you, but it certainly has not been proven that this Jewish captain wrote that letter. Even if the handwriting does resemble the Jew's—what of that? The one who wrote the letter may have imitated the Jewish captain's handwriting. The matter certainly ought to be thoroughly examined," and a troubled look came into his face.

"Well, well," the elderly man chuckled, "if I didn't know your parents, André, I would think you were a Jew yourself. No proof is needed to make me believe that a Jew is a traitor."

"But Grandpa," came the voice of a boy in front of him, "The captain's brother has clear proof that a certain officer in the French army (I think his name is Esterhazy) was the one who really wrote that letter. This Esterhazy was a spy paid by the German government. So even if the captain is a Jew, I think it's only fair to give him a new trial."

Tearfully the grandson looked up at his grandfather. He didn't know what to expect.

Just then the crowd roared again, "Down with the traitor," as Captain Alfred Dreyfus, the Jew, was marched swiftly down the field between his two guards.

A special ceremony to humiliate the captain had been prepared. He was ordered to step up on a platform. Then a lieu-

tenant came up and broke his sword. While the crowd cheered
a sergeant stepped up and stripped Dreyfus of his epaulettes.
Finally came a corporal who tore off the buttons of his uniform,
one by one, and cast them at the feet of the unfortunate Dreyfus.

All this time Dreyfus kept repeating over and over: "I did
not write that letter. I never sold any secrets to the German
government." With blood-shot eyes and white face he pleaded:
"Surely someone will find out what a terrible mistake has been
made. I am innocent—innocent, I tell you!"

And when the mob shouted: "Death to the traitor," Captain
Dreyfus cried: "Long live France! Long live the army!"

But in spite of all his pleas, Captain Dreyfus, cruelly dis-
honored, was ordered to life imprisonment on Devil's Island.

Suddenly there was a lull in the cheering and hissing of the
crowd. A young man, dark and handsome, with a kingly bearing, was making his way to the platform. A few yards away he
stopped to speak to a friend. Tears stood in his deep-set eyes. He
had a beautifully modelled head.

The crowd was attracted by the unforgettable appearance of
this man, who seemed to hold them as if by some magic power.
"Who is that?" they whispered to one another. For Theodor
Herzl was not yet known to Jew or Gentile in France. He had
just been sent from Vienna as a reporter for an important
Vienna newspaper. And the most important news at that time
was the Dreyfus affair. Herzl took out his little notebook and
jotted something down.

Dr. Nordau, the famous author to whom Herzl was speaking, grew pale as the crowd shouted with glee. With trembling lips he turned to Herzl and asked: "Why must they be so brutal? How can they be so happy at a man's suffering? Even a traitor is a human being."

Herzl of the kingly appearance looked sharply at Nordau as he replied: "But they refuse to treat Dreyfus as a human being. The French see Dreyfus not as a man, but as a Jew. As a Jew he is at their mercy, because the Jews have no country of their own."

Herzl again stopped to write in his book. He was probably taking notes for his article to send back to Vienna. Herzl was a writer, but he had not yet written anything important. If this man of the remarkable appearance was born to be a king, he had not yet found his kingdom. If he was to be a prophet, he had not yet seen the great Vision. Only his appearance was unusual.

Herzl then said to Nordau with deep feeling: "Yes, dear friend, it is not Dreyfus who is being humiliated, but the whole Jewish people. Dreyfus is only a symbol—a sign."

His eyes became dreamy, as if he were suddenly far away. They shone with a deep, sad glow. Then, with sudden haste, he added:

"Excuse me, I must hurry home. I have some very urgent, very important work to do."

Dr. Nordau gazed after him. He would have liked to ask Herzl whether something ailed him. But, somehow, one doesn't

TODROS
GELLER.

become intimate with a king or a prophet, even if he is one's friend.

There was in Herzl's eyes that far-off gaze into the future. Perhaps he was beginning to see the Vision—the Dream.

*   *   *

Herzl hurried home and in a fever of excitement called his little girl into his study.

"Do you see that typewriter on my desk, Pauline?" he asked. "Do you know what we call it?"

"Yes, Father, you call it your 'portable' typewriter."

"Do you know why?" Herzl asked again. And without waiting for a reply, answered, "Because I can carry it with me, wherever I go. Now, it's almost like that with the Jews and their homeland. Their homeland is like a portable typewriter."

"How can they carry a whole land?" Pauline asked simply.

"They can't carry a land, my dear, but they do carry their ideas and their spirit in books. That is not good either. It is like a soul flitting about without a body. Just as a soul must have a body, the Jewish people must have a land, a Jewish State."

"Yes, of course!" Pauline said with certainty, wondering why her father was so excited.

"You know the story of the 'Second Purim,' which took place in Damascus, and you know the story of the First Purim which took place in Persia. To-night you will hear about the Dreyfus affair, which took place right here in Paris."

"So will we have a Third Purim?" Pauline, who was a bright child, asked.

Frau Herzl had entered and was listening silently. She smiled when Pauline asked that question, but Herzl continued to talk quickly.

"These affairs can all be stopped, if the Jews only will it—if the *whole* Jewish people wants it. Mordecai Manuel Noah and Judah Touro of America couldn't do it. Moses Montefiore of England couldn't do it. No one man can do it by himself."

Herzl suddenly looked up at his wife. She was alarmed at his appearance. But she dared not interrupt him. And indeed nobody *could* interrupt him! Herzl went right on:

"Do you know why Touro's and Montefiore's plans failed? Because they gave charity, charity to poor Jews. They did not have the idea of building up the Jewish people—the whole Jewish people. Can you imagine, Pauline, what would happen if I felt that I were giving charity to you and Mamma and Grandma?"

"That would make us beggars," Pauline replied and, turning to her mother, asked, "Do we feel like beggars?"

"Of course not! We are one family, all trying to make one another happy," Frau Herzl sighed.

"And you are *not* beggars. I belong to you, and you belong to me. I couldn't live without you. And I want to help you in every way. Unless each Jew feels that the whole Jewish people belongs to him: unless each Jew, when he gives his money, feels that he is building a home for his own people, and not giving charity to strangers, we shall never be able to build a homeland!"

Frau Herzl was alarmed at her husband's excitement. She said quietly: "Come, Pauline, it is bedtime," and taking the child by the hand, led her out of the room.

As she closed the door she heard Herzl murmur: "It's all so clear to me now. It's becoming remarkably clear. Zion must become a Jewish State. And I shall devote my life to making that dream come true. I shall die, but the idea of Zion will live on forever."

With feverish haste Herzl began to write down his ideas. For weeks he didn't interrupt his writing, except to eat and sleep. His wife called one of his best friends to the house. Herzl read him the pamphlet which he had written.

As the friend read, his eyes filled with tears. This didn't seem strange to Herzl. He himself had wept when he had written his pamphlet, "The Jewish State."

But then the friend turned to Frau Herzl and they spoke in whispers. Herzl realized that they both thought he was insane.

Still, Herzl plucked up courage and, pointing to the pamphlet, asked: "What do you think of it?"

The friend, looking searchingly at Herzl, asked: "So you think you can organize all the Jews to carry out your idea?"

"It's not *my* idea. It's the lot of the Jew. It's that which the Jewish people must do. And if they will it, it will be done." Herzl's face glowed with enthusiasm as he spoke.

"Please give up this notion or you will be considered a lunatic," the friend pleaded.

"You are like a cold wind that suddenly blows out a flame which has just been kindled," Herzl answered sorrowfully. All the light went out of his eyes.

"All right," he said. His head sank on his chest. "I'll give up the idea."

A few days later, Herzl turned to his wife and said firmly, as if he had made a sudden decision, "Julie, pack up. We will return to Vienna. I can work better there. Yes, Julie dear, the more they try to discourage me, the harder I will work. I will not give up."

In spite of the advice of his wife and his friend, Herzl began to give his money, his time and energy, and his very life to his dream of Zionism.

*   *   *

"This new Messiah—tell me, is he coming on a white horse?" asked one English Jew mockingly.

"Or perhaps on a seven-headed dragon?" asked another, winking to his friends.

"No, he just rides in a motor-car," answered Zangwill the famous Jewish author, good-humoredly.

The train was moving so fast that Zangwill couldn't read. He closed his book and joined the conversation.

"The Jews of Bulgaria and Poland look to Herzl as to a

Messiah. And he does resemble Sabbatai Zevi," Zangwill re-marked.

"But they won't let Herzl have a conference in Munich, Ger-many. The Jews of Germany don't want Herzl's idea."

"Then he'll go to Basle in Switzerland. It's probably a pret-tier spot," Zangwill smiled. "Haven't you read the invitation Herzl has sent out?" And with that Zangwill produced a copy from his coat pocket:

"To Jews in countries all over the world:

"You are invited to send delegates to represent the Jewish Nation on August 5, 1897, to Basle, Switzerland. We shall come out of the Ghetto. We shall proclaim our right to live our own life—in our own land. Can you think of a greater, more festive holiday? So put on your holiday clothes. Dress to suit the occasion."

"That's rather funny!—Ha, ha, a Messiah worried about clothes!"

"Why, no, I don't think it funny! Herzl himself is hand-some. He likes to do things beautifully. He wants to make our people beautiful inside and out."

The train had arrived at Basle. Zangwill shook hands with the mocking Englishmen and went to find the hotel, where Herzl had called the first Zionist Congress.

Zangwill hastened to a seat just as Theodor Herzl, towering like a real king in Israel, rose to lay before the Assembly the plans which he had outlined in his book, *The Jewish State.*

"We shall make it our will to establish a home for the Jews in Palestine. It will be a land that shall be recognized by all nations and all governments as the lawful home of the Jews." Herzl's voice rang out, clear as a silver bell. He seemed enchanted, and indeed he cast a spell on all those present.

"I propose that we form a society of Jews. They will work out the details of the plan. We must also form a Jewish company, which will raise one quarter of a billion dollars with which to take the Jews to Palestine after the land has been bought. We shall organize commerce and industry, build bridges, railways and houses."

Then a delegate arose and said: "I move that the society of Jews be called The Zionist Organization, and that the Jewish company be called The Jewish Colonial Trust. I suggest that every Jew pay a shekel (25c) yearly and thus become a member of the Zionist Organization."

Then in a quiet, dignified manner another delegate said: "We must establish a Jewish National Fund in order to buy the land of Palestine for the Jews. We shall not shed blood to get the land. We shall *buy* it. The land so bought will then belong to the whole Jewish people and not to private individuals."

It was some time since Herzl had spoken. The spell seemed to have worn off. A voice from the gallery cried:

"How will you secure a charter from the Sultan?"

"How will you persuade all the countries to agree?" chuckled another.

The disorder spread. "How will you get every Jew to pay a shekel?"

"No rich Jew will like your plan," came from another corner.

Herzl then arose. A silence fell. Prophet-like he spoke:

"We don't want rich Jews who do not believe in our cause. Nor do we want poor Jews who do not understand our aim. We want rich Jews who will give, and give generously to build a nation. We want poor Jews who will work, and work hard to build a nation.

"May I tell you a story?" Herzl asked with a smile. Then he said,

"Once there was an Arab who was very patient and slow to anger. One morning he started out from his village to the city, carrying a calf. As he was walking along cheerfully he met a man who asked, 'Where are you carrying your calf?'

"The Arab answered, 'To the city, good friend, God be with you.'

"He had not gone on very far when a second man passed and asked: 'Whither are you carrying your calf?'

"The Arab answered again: 'To the city, good friend, God be with you."

"Then after a while there came a third and a fourth and a fifth and asked him the same question. The Arab, being patient, always answered in a friendly tone, 'To the city, good friend, God be with you.'

"But by the time the Arab had answered 15 or 20 men, his patience gave way. The answer became shorter. He now said, 'To the city, good friend.' After repeating this about a dozen times even this became too much. To the next man who asked him, he answered shortly, 'To the city.' His voice became more and more unfriendly until it became rude.

"The Arab began to think that people had joined in a conspiracy to make a fool of him. And when the hundredth man asked him, 'Whither are you carrying your calf?' the Arab thought he saw a mocking smile on his lips. Whereupon he set down the calf, caught the man by the throat and began to strangle him.

"We Zionists are in the same position as the Arab with the calf. We are forever being asked the same questions, and we are gradually becoming impatient.

"But I want to tell those of you who are our friends that the people who ask the question are always *new* passers-by, and they have not yet had an explanation. Let us always try, peacefully, to give them the answer. And let us remember that the oftener we have answered the question, the nearer we have carried our calf to the city.

"Of course there will be some people, whom we have already answered once, who will come boldly and ask again; or there will be those who will say, 'It's not true. You're *not* going to the city'; or 'The city just doesn't exist'; or 'I am not your friend, and God will *not* be with you.' When we meet such people, we shall simply turn our backs on them and say to ourselves, 'Soon we shall be in the city.'"

"Soon we shall be in the city." The whole hall resounded as Herzl sat down.

And Herzl began to carry out his plans. Herzl went to the Pope. The Pope did not like Herzl's plan at all. The Pope thought that Palestine should not be a Jewish state. But Herzl was not discouraged.

Herzl renewed his energy and went to the German Emperor. The Emperor's answer was neither yes nor no. Still Herzl was happy that the Emperor had allowed him to present his plan at all.

Herzl's health was giving way. He began to have symptoms of heart disease. But nothing could make him give up his work. He thought of nothing else, night and day!

Herzl went to St. Petersburg. The Czar did not care how many Jews left Russia. But there were to be no Zionists in Russia. Still Herzl kept on with his task.

His heart was getting weaker all the time. Yet he went to Turkey.

Herzl had no money to offer the Sultan for a charter, but he tried to convince him to allow the Jews to have Palestine as their home. The Sultan agreed to let the Jews come in singly but not as a whole people.

Herzl visited Italy, Poland, Russia, Bulgaria and Turkey.

The Dream had not yet come true, but Herzl had come

much closer "to the city," to Palestine. He gave all his time, his money and his energy to make his dream come true.

* * *

It was after the Sixth Congress. Herzl, worn and weary, had taken to his bed. His secretary, Mr. Reich, was with him. Herzl would doze for a while, and then would awake with a start. Mr. Reich read him some letters from his children. Herzl dozed off again.

Suddenly his fingers plucked nervously at the quilt. He sat up in bed and cried to his secretary, "Listen, Reich—this land here," and he drew a line around a circle on the quilt—"The National Fund must buy this land."

He sank back on his pillows, never to rise again. But his spirit is still alive in the hearts of many Jews throughout the world.

The Hidden Treasure

"A MYSTERY! A mystery!" Dr. Schechter exclaimed as he paced up and down his spacious library. "But I shall solve it!"

His wife and children started up at the words.

"A mystery? What is it? What is it?" the children cried, one after another.

Without seeming to have heard them at all, Dr. Schechter continued:

"It may be that some have been buried alive." He was apparently relieved at this thought.

But his family shuddered: "Horrors! No! What is it, Father?" cried his eldest.

"That means it will be easier to put it together!"

"Put it together!" The family looked at each other bewildered.

"Yes, this page here is a limb, a disjointed limb. This page is a scrap, a fragment out of the book of Ben Sira; and I am determined to find the whole body."

217

"Oh, father!" one of the children burst out laughing. "That is interesting, but you had us scared for a while."

"I didn't mean to do that," Dr. Schechter said as his sparkling blue eyes danced with joy. His beard seemed redder than usual.

"Mrs. Lewis and Mrs. Gibson have just given me this scrap which they bought on their last trip to Palestine. I recognized it immediately as a page out of this famous Book of Ben Sira which was not put into the Bible, but into a collection called the *Apocrypha*. You can't imagine how impatient I was to get home in order to find out whether I was right."

"How do you know now?" asked Dr. Schechter's oldest son.

"That's a fine question. You see, there is a Greek translation of this book."

"Oh! A translation! How do you know it's a translation?"

Dr. Schechter smiled as he pinched his son's cheek: "I see you want to become a detective like your father. That's fine! You will be a great help. We know that the Greek book is a translation because the man who wrote it tells us that. Besides I, myself, have found many references to it in the Talmud. And these references show that there was such a book in Hebrew over a thousand years ago. But alas! that book got lost!" Dr. Schechter heaved a deep sigh as if his best friend had passed away.

The children smiled, but Frank, his oldest son, was not yet

satisfied. He asked, "Father, why are you so interested in this book?"

"Because if we could find this book—that is, the Hebrew original of it, we could learn a lot about Jewish history that we don't know now."

Mrs. Schechter smiled as she proudly explained: "If it were not for the work of such men as your father, we should never increase our knowledge of Jewish History."

But the children had stopped listening to their mother. They were more interested in learning how Dr. Schechter would go about finding the body of this missing book.

"But how? How are you going to find out? That seems like detective work!"

Dr. Schechter stroked his beard and said, as if to himself, "This much we know:

"For centuries the Jews have treated their torn Hebrew books with the same respect as they would treat the body of a person who had died. The story is told that when Rabbi Chaninah ben Teradyon was to be burnt at the stake, wrapped in the scrolls of the law, he said: 'I see the parchment burning, but the letters are flying up to heaven.' What he meant was that though the body of a book is gone, the spirit goes to heaven like the spirit of a human being.

"Therefore, just as the Jews bury their dead, so they bury the loose pages of a book. Sometimes, however, a book is only sick, that is, only some of its pages are missing. Such books

are hidden away. The hiding place for the books is called in
Hebrew Genizah, or treasure house. There are many such Genizahs. Every large synagogue has a Genizah."

Dr. Schechter looked around to see whether his family understood him. Noting their rapt attention he continued,

"Of course, when we know this much we must get clues and
trace them."

Mrs. Schechter and the children listened, wide-eyed. Frank
suggested, "Then you have to go to one of these Genizah's to
search for Ben Sira. Isn't that it, Daddy? I get the idea!"

"Right. But the question is, which one? We think it very
likely that it may be in some Genizah in Palestine or in Egypt,
because that is where our most ancient communities were."

"Then you have to go through each one of those Genizahs!"
another son suggested.

"No. I shall first try to find some clues. I'll publish an article on this fragment which I have here."

"How will that help?" asked another one of the children,
completely at a loss to understand.

"You'll see," Dr. Schechter replied, beaming with joy.

"First I must send a telegram to Mrs. Lewis and Mrs. Gibson to let them know of their great find. Then I shall write an
article on the 'Fragment of Ben Sira.'"

That week the whole Schechter family could hardly eat or
sleep. They were burning with impatience to see the article
in print, and eager to know what clues it might bring.

The article was published, and daily, when Dr. Schechter returned from Cambridge University, where he was teaching, they would shower him with questions.

"Is there a clue today, Daddy? What is it?" And one day the answer was forthcoming.

"Yes, there is a clue, and more than one. Just as I had hoped, the article led Dr. Neubauer and Dr. Cowley to search Hebrew manuscripts in the Bodleian Library, which is a famous library here in England. They found some more fragments of Ben Sira. They all point to writings in the 11th century."

The children and even Mrs. Schechter looked blank. How would that give a clue to the Genizah?

"Don't you see? Now I have to find out if there is a synagogue which has a history that goes back that far."

"Oh," the oldest son clapped his hands, "that's great, Dad! Then you will go to the Genizah of that synagogue?"

"That is exactly what I hope to do."

Dr. Schechter learned that the synagogue in Cairo, Egypt, known as the synagogue of Ezra the Scribe was thought to be the oldest in the Orient. And so he set out for Cairo in search of the Hidden Treasure, the Book of Ben Sira.

"What is a real Genizah?" "What does it look like?" "Will Dr. Schechter be successful?" Such were the questions, not only of Dr. Schechter's family, but of many Jewish scholars and scientists throughout the world.

* * *

It was a cold day in December, 1896, when Dr. Schechter arrived in Cairo. As he rode from the station to the hotel he was impressed with the modern appearance of the streets and buildings. There were no pyramids, no ancient structures. Nothing to tell of the glory of the past. His heart sank. It was all so modern.

"And this is the place," Dr. Schechter thought sadly, "from which I expect to return with ancient spoils." His head seemed to grow shaggier as he hopelessly shrugged his shoulders.

The president of the community introduced Dr. Schechter to the important people of the city. He then took him to the famous synagogue of Ezra the Scribe. As they were walking toward the synagogue, the president was telling Dr. Schechter its history.

"In some writings it is called the synagogue of Elijah and Jeremiah. It has a history that extends over more than a thousand years."

At these words Dr. Schechter looked at the president so intently with his piercing blue eyes that the president had to lower his own. There was something keen and prophetic in Dr. Schechter's gaze.

The president continued: "Since the Mohammedans conquered Egypt the temple has been in possession of the Jews."

Dr. Schechter became more hopeful. The president took him through the synagogue and at last to the Genizah, which was at the end of the gallery. It looked like a large room without either windows or doors. A ladder was brought in. Soon Dr. Schechter was climbing up the rungs to a big, shapeless hole which was the entrance to the Genizah. As he climbed he couldn't help thinking what a thrill it would give his children to climb with him. When he approached the top it seemed to Dr. Schechter he heard a voice saying:

"This is our resting place!" Dr. Schechter wondered, "Who could be speaking?"

"It's the resting place for us books," the Voice continued, "the books that have been produced for many centuries. Now we lie in this hole, broken, torn and aching."

At last Dr. Schechter entered the Genizah. Though it was very dark he noticed a big yellow Bible, without covers and with its binding torn loose. It seemed to Dr. Schechter that the Bible was saying,

"Some of the books couldn't stand this air at all. They perished immediately. Others were crushed to death for want of space. Still others have been so tightly squeezed together that even instruments couldn't separate them without hurting them."

As Dr. Schechter picked up the Bible, clouds of dust flew into the air. He began to cough and sneeze.

"Why did it stop talking? I wish I knew more about these books," Dr. Schechter thought aloud. Then a Voice said:

"We on the top here really don't have so much to tell. You see, we were put here not so very long ago."

Dr. Schechter spent his days in the Genizah and came
y at night, for food. The dust from the old volumes
im look old and gray. It had settled in his throat and
ting into his lungs. His health was failing so that he
accept the help of the warden of the Genizah.

lly, after Dr. Schechter had made very careful arrange-
or the shipment of hundreds of baskets of pages, he re-
to England. He did not go home, but hastened to the
dge Basement Library where the baskets had been de-
There his family met him. His children did not know
hey were happier to see, their father or those old, old
om the Genizah.

t, Father," they exclaimed, "how gray you have be-

her, how old you look!" exclaimed another.

. Schechter smiled as she wiped away a tear: "But think
all this work will mean for the Jewish people! We shall
out Jewish prayer. It will help us to understand Jewish

his time the children had become used to the change in
her's appearance. They suddenly formed a ring around
d began to sing: "Hail the Great Detective! Hail the
Detective!"

he midst of their mirth their father said sadly, "But I
yet put that book together. I haven't yet made the body

Dr. Schechter pushed his way
farthest end of the hole. His eyes w
was dry.

"That's it," a Voice said, "now
direction. We have been here for
us for three hundred, some for six
a thousand years. But, of course,
and yellower we are, and the hard

Another voice interrupted: "Ye
law suits, marriage contracts, medi
They are not sacred books like us.

Dr. Schechter picked up a hea
carefully to separate them.

"Ouch!" he heard a cry. "Eve
you're hurting us. We are pasted
holy pages among us, too."

Dr. Schechter trembled with h
the pile of pages in a large basket
purpose.

"Here is life," he thought. "W
odds and ends will tell when the
put together. However, it's imposs
to England. I guess I'll take only
are older and so much more imp

Every leaf, every scrap of pap
torn book was carefully packed

month
out on
made
was ge
had to
Fin
ments
turned
Cambr
posited
which
pages f
"Bi
come!'
"Fa
Mr:
of wha
learn a
history
By
their fa
him an
Great
In
haven't
whole.'

The children stopped. Their spirits drooped.

"What! You did not secure that Book of Ben Sira?"

"No, not yet! And maybe I never shall see it whole! You see these thousands of boxes and stacks. Each box contains single leaves or sheets. They have many different systems of writings. For instance there is one where the writing seems to extend below the line. From this writing we get an idea at about what period that leaf was written."

Frank snatched the paper excitedly from his father's hand. "Please, Father, let me see if I can find another sheet written like that."

Dr. Schechter was glad to see his son's intelligent interest.

"Here is another very interesting thing," Dr. Schechter continued. "Do you see that yellow mark on the leaf? It is different in shape from the rest of the writing, isn't it?"

"Yes," the children agreed as they gathered around their father.

"That's called a palimpsest. It means a sheet on which there was first one kind of writing, then that writing was erased and something else written in the same space. So we can read not only what we see there now, but from the back of the Sheet we read what has been erased! That, you see, is more than a double sheet!"

"Why—that's magic, father!"

"Now I shall begin the task of separating, classifying, and arranging all these pages."

"I can help, father," said Frank.

"And I," cried the other son.

"Me, too," cried the youngest.

"Yes. You will all help; and many scholars will help; and still the work will not be completed," Dr. Schechter sighed sadly.

"But our Rabbis have said, "Though you cannot hope to finish the work, you must not give it up."

For five years Dr. Schechter worked on the Genizah. At the end of that time he had put together the Book of Ben Sira.

There were still hundreds of pages left. There was still much knowledge to be gained from these pages.

When Dr. Schechter was called to America in 1901 to become the President of the Jewish Theological Seminary in New York, he again transferred his beloved Genizah. This time it went with him to New York.

But Dr. Schechter loved his Judaism and Jews even more, perhaps, than his work on the Genizah. And so he took time from his detective work to create the United Synagogue of America. He also put the Jewish Theological Seminary of America on a solid foundation. At the same time he tried to continue the work of the Genizah. No one can tell, yet, which was his most important work.

The Rebel

"Tramp! Tramp! Tramp! Those are soldiers marching!" Little Chaim Nachman said to himself when the rebbi (teacher) showed him, first a line of "alephs" (א), then a line of "beths" (ב) and then a third line of letters with a "segol" under each (בֶ).

"Those surely are soldiers, armed from head to foot," thought Chaim Nachman Bialik.

The line of gimmels (ג) seemed to be all set for the march. They seemed to be marking time with the right foot. Right—right. Without realizing it, Chaim Nachman began to swing his head and hand, and beat time with his foot.

"That won't do, Chaim Nachman," the rebbi scolded. "You'll never learn anything that way."

"Now look here! See this?" The rebbi picked up a large single card with the letter aleph printed on it. "Do you see the rod here, and the two pails?" (א)

229

"Right!" Chaim exclaimed, enjoying the idea.

"Now that is an aleph."

"Now that is an aleph," Chaim repeated.

"What is this?" the rebbi asked, as he pointed to the card.

"An axle with two pails," Chaim replied quickly.

"No! Say aleph. Remember—aleph. Aleph."

On his way home from school Chaim met Martha, one of the servant girls, walking along balancing a pole over her shoulders, with a pail of water at each end of it.

The next day at school the rebbi took up the "aleph" card and asked, "What is this?"

Chaim Nachman answered quickly, "Oh, that's Martha!" happy with his discovery.

And so to Chaim Nachman every letter of the alphabet looked like some interesting creature, fish or fowl or animal. The worst of it was that sometimes the same letter would once look like a fish, and another time like a dog. How would Chaim Nachman ever learn his letters?

So, while with his lips Chaim Nachman was repeating the words of the rebbi, with his imagination he was immediately turning them into something else. Sometimes the letters made Chaim think of such funny things, he simply couldn't help laughing out loud. That made the rebbi very angry. Chaim never could understand why his laughter angered the rebbi. But he tried hard not to laugh aloud again.

Soon recess came. All the children would go out to play,

but not Chaim. In a quiet spot, hidden from the rest of the children, Chaim would sit and go over the alphabet and notice what funny things he could see in the letters. Here Chaim could laugh as long and as loud as he pleased. Here neither the rebbi nor the children would disturb him.

But when the boys announced that they were going to tell stories, then Chaim did join them. One of the stories they told was about a miracle man who lived long ago. This miracle man could perform all kinds of wonders. Among other things, he could draw milk from a wall. (If he cared to, he could become as mighty and as powerful as the Lord himself.) This idea charmed Chaim Nachman. Fancy drawing milk from a wall!

All that afternoon Chaim Nachman sat in his class. But his mind was on things far, far away. He was busy making plans for the milking.

At last school was over. Chaim ran through the path he had made in the thick woods of Radi. That was a little village near Zhitomir where Chaim lived. Chaim Nachman ran into the house and into the pantry where the milk dishes were kept. If the wall was going to spout milk he would have to have dishes to receive it. Carefully Chaim planned every step. He would not take the good dishes. Those might be missed. So Chaim chose pots without handles, and bowls with cracks in them. He even found a cork to put in the wall to stop the flow of the milk. Who could tell—the dishes might not be sufficient to hold all the milk he would get!

This done, Chaim then began to walk through the house, carefully examining all the walls. Which would be the best for milking? He would tap a wall and then put his ear to it, listening intently, just as a doctor does when he examines a patient's chest.

At last Chaim found the spot! It seemed whiter and gave back a different sound than had any other spot on the walls. Chaim brought all the dishes which he had so carefully prepared. The cork he placed close by. Everything seemed safe and ready. Chaim then placed a pot in front of the spot, and kneeling on the floor began to tap with his right hand. He tapped lightly. The spot seemed to be turning whiter.

"It must be that the milk is beginning to come up," Chaim thought. In his eagerness he began knocking instead of tapping the wall. The spot was growing whiter all the time. Unable to wait any longer Chaim took one of the frying pans and banged it against the wall with all his might.

Just at that moment, at the very moment when it seemed to Chaim the milk was beginning to spurt, Chaim felt a slap on his cheek, so swift and sudden that he dropped the pot. His father had come up from behind him.

"The milk—the milk," Chaim Nachman cried, bewildered.

"What are you up to now? What are all these pots doing here? And why do you wreck the house?" his father scolded. "Now just look at the hole you have made in the wall! Look at that plaster crumbling!"

"Yes, I guess you are right, Father," Chaim answered between sobs. It is only plaster and not milk. You are right. I'll never be a miracle worker—only a wrecker!"

"But he who wrecks may also build," said Chaim's father gently, his anger gone.

*　　*　　*

"So said Rabbi Akiba."

"So replied Rabbi Chaninah."

The students chanted the words of the Talmud in a singsong manner. They tried hard to understand the explanations given by the rabbis.

"Chaim, will you explain this passage?"

Chaim Nachman wrinkled his brow. His face turned red.

"Well, let me see," Chaim blushed and stammered.

Chaim was now a young man. He was attending a Y'shivo College to which his grandfather had sent him.

The truth was that Chaim had hidden a modern Hebrew novel between the covers of the Talmud. He was trying to read this book and study the Talmud at the same time.

Chaim tried to explain the sentence. Then suddenly he stopped. Flushed with anger he took out the hidden book and showed it to the "Rosh Y'shivo" (teacher).

"I might as well tell the truth!" he said defiantly. "I have been trying to read this book. And I have been studying Russian, too. The other boys are doing the same thing. We've organized a club, called the Eternal Israel, and we've made up our minds that we are through. We don't want to be shut away here any longer.

"For six years we haven't seen a blade of green grass. For six years we haven't seen a ray of sunlight. For six years we have been buried here among these heavy volumes, studying and studying. The desk, the candle and the book have been our only companions. For six years we have studied nothing but the dry Talmud. For six years we have been sitting here as if there were no lakes for swimming, no snow for sledding. It's time we gave up this life in the Y'shivo and went out to see sunlight."

The other students sat, silent, as Chaim Nachman Bialik, the most brilliant of them all, closed the Talmud with a bang, and, putting the modern volume under his arm, left the room.

Not a single one of them was able to think of his studies after that. As soon as they were dismissed, they rushed out to look for Bialik. They found him sitting on the little hill they called "Yarmulka" because it was shaped like a skull cap. This spot was the secret meeting-place of the club. Chaim was sitting on a rock with pencil and paper, writing and erasing; writing and erasing.

The boys went up to Chaim and watched him silently. Finally one of his friends said jokingly, "Make up your mind, Chaim, which do you want to do, erasing or writing?"

Chaim smiled. "I have erased plenty. I'm afraid I shall always try to write, and so I shall always have to erase. Yes, 200 lines erased," Chaim sighed as he looked at the paper before him. "200 lines erased for one line left. But if this is to be read by our people, a people which is to live forever—then only perfect things must be written for them. And that takes time."

"Please read us those lines," said another boy. Chaim read:

TO THE BIRD *

Bird on my window perching,
Returned from the land of the sun,
Blessed be this thy coming,
For now is the winter done.

Sweet is the sound of thy singing,
For I, abandoned, in vain
Longed through the weary winter
To hear thee again.

Sing, bird, for full is thy singing
Of marvelous tidings and dear,
And tell me if there in the sun-land
Life is as bitter as here.

Greeting thou bringest from Zion,
From loved ones who wait for me there;
Ah, happy ones! Surely they know not
How heavy the burden I bear.

How fierce are my enemies round me,
Countless against me they rise,

* From *Selected Poems*, by Chaim Nachman Bialik. Translated by Maurice Samuel. New Palestine 1926.

For there in the land of their dwelling
Spring never dies.

Singing thou bringest me greeting
From the vale and the mountain head.
Has God now remembered Zion,
Or weeps she still o'er her dead?

In the gloom of the valley of Sharon
Is the myrrh still as rich as of yore?
Are the cedars awaking from slumber
In Lebanon, dreaming and hoar?

Is Hermon still covered with pearls
When the dew of the morning distils?
And what news of the waters of Jordan?
What news of the ancient hills?

Has the shadow of death departed
And the cloud been lifted at last
From the land of my fathers' dwelling,
From the land where my youth was passed?

Are the trees yet green and blooming
I planted in sacred mould?
Like them I was once in blossom,
But now I am withered and old.

Sing of the breadth of meadows
And secrets the grasses told,
Of the time when the corn in fulness
Shall change their green to gold.

My brothers have sown in tears,
Weeping the seed they cast;
Is the time of their labor ended?
Shall they reap in joy at last?

And I, what news can I give thee;
What exchange for thy tidings, bird?
Not songs, for here in the Northlands
Only the storm is heard.

Of pain I can tell, and labor,
And rest that is yet unfound,
Of sorrow added to sorrow
And mourning with mourning crowned.

Happy art thou whom the desert
And the tops of the mountains await,
For beside me the joy of thy singing
Would change into tears for my fate.

And tears will not comfort or strengthen,
Tears will not soften the smart,
For old are these eyes now with weeping,
And withered with weeping my heart.

Though time that ends all has not ended
The ancient tale of my wrong,
Yet blessed art thou in thy coming,
And happy shall be thy song.

To Bialik's surprise, the boys applauded.

"That's real poetry, Chaim. You'll be a great man, a great

poet, the 'mouthpiece' of our people," one of his friends said enthusiastically.

Then Chaim Nachman announced: "My mind is made up. I'm planning to go to Odessa. I want to meet Achad Ha'am and the other great men there."

"Will your grandfather send you the money?" asked Joseph.

"No. He doesn't know I'm going. He wouldn't let me go if he knew. I guess I'll have to sell my books. Ever since I was seven years old all my extra pennies have gone to buy books. Maybe now, by selling them, I shall have enough for the trip. And after that?" Chaim Nachman Bialik answered his own question. "God will provide."

A few days later, more than a hundred students said farewell at the station to their beloved friend and leader, Chaim Nachman. With heavy hearts, though with high hopes for their friend, they watched the train pull out.

* * *

It was an unusually busy day at Ravnitsky's Publishing House. One more day and their magazine was to go to press. Still, the material was not ready. Everybody was hurrying.

In the midst of the excitement a strange young man entered. It was clear that he was nervous. One could see that the hand in which he held a little notebook was trembling. The editor, Ravnitsky, looked through the office window and smiled at the man on his left.

"Here comes another genius! Can we close our door to geniuses? Anyway, since we are sadly in need of a few more items for our magazine, we had better see the young man."

Saying this, Mr. Ravnitsky motioned to Chaim Nachman Bialik to come in. Though Bialik had eaten very little for an entire week, he did not look starved. His childhood days spent in the green fields and the woods had made him healthy.

Ravnitsky took the notebook which Bialik had brought. He knew exactly what to expect. All the young Russian Jewish writers came to him. All of them thought they were geniuses.

Ravnitsky, expecting little, glanced over the first stanza of the poem, "To the Bird." Then, with suddenly increased interest, he read the rest of the poem. Ravnitsky looked searchingly at Bialik and asked: "You wrote this, young man?"

Bialik blushed and stammered: "Y-y-yes."

"Here is something different," Ravnitsky said over his shoulder to his assistant. "Read this. I shall give this young fellow a letter of introduction to Achad Ha'am. It may be we have really discovered a genius this time."

Bialik, hardly able to believe his own ears, took the letter in his hand. Again he began to stammer and blush, and, stumbling over his own feet, left the office of Ravnitsky.

It was not long before Bialik had become a famous poet.

The blushing Chaim Nachman, of the little village of Radi, the most brilliant rebel-student of the Y'shivo, became the greatest Jewish poet—the Poet of the People.

Adventures in the Desert

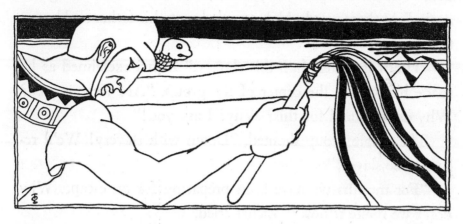

"Whip him! Lash him! The day's work does not end with the setting of the sun." The taskmaster spoke through set teeth.

"I am human, and I will not be treated like a beast," Zichri, the Jewish slave, cried rebelliously. "This will be the last lashing I will take from you!"

"Zichri has been giving a lot of trouble. He refuses to obey commands," another taskmaster added. And Zichri was taken out for a beating.

No sooner was the lashing over than Zichri forced himself up with all his might. He dragged himself over to the campfire of the slaves. As soon as his wife and his son, Abihu, noticed Zichri they ran over to him.

"Where have you been? What has kept you?" they asked, with fear in their eyes.

With trembling lips Zichri said: "I've been where I hope never to be again." With pale face and flashing eyes he continued, "Neither I nor any of you here will enter that lashing hut again." At these words Abihu nestled up to his father and began to cry.

"Death is better than this slavery," Zichri exclaimed as he made his way to the center of the group. "Are we not men? Why do we stand for this? Why? I ask you!"

The whole group shouted, "Down with slavery! We'll refuse to be slaves!"

"For months we have been preparing for an escape. Why don't we make it now?" Zichri cried.

At this, a woman replied, "What? Where shall we go? To the desert?"

A few of the men answered sadly as they shook their heads and shrugged their shoulders, "We can't leave Egypt yet. We mustn't leave Egypt yet. The Lord doesn't want us to!"

"Now, Zichri," pleaded an old man softly, "we can't go against the will of the Lord."

"We won't go against the Lord, we'll march on to the Promised Land. And if we must go through the desert, we'll do that! March on," Zichri shouted, "On to the Promised Land!"

"On to the Promised Land," the men and women echoed his words. The women and children left the camp fire for the tents. All the children, except Abihu and his cousin Jachin. If exciting things were going to happen, they wanted to be on hand.

Zichri now began to give last minute instructions.

"When the moon comes up in the sky and the women and the guards are asleep, we shall steal away singly. You, Eliphaz, will take care of the weapons: the quivers, the hammers, the arrows, the spears, the javelins and the swords. You, Nadab, will load the camels." And so Zichri went around the circle, giving final instructions for the march.

"Father," Abihu called, as his father passed him by. "Do let Jachin and me help. We are going along too, you know."

"Of course, we're going too," repeated Jachin rather sleepily.

Zichri looked at his son and nephew, his eyes filling with tears. "This will not be a pleasure trip, Abi. This will not be a simple march, Jachin. Who knows—we may never reach the Promised Land."

Abi, who had been listening intently, said, "But in the desert we'll be free!"

"Yes, we'll be free—but you had better go to Mother. When we reach the Promised Land, we'll send for you."

But Abihu clung to his father's hand. "I won't leave you, father. I don't want to grow up as a slave. I will help all I can. I will gather the water skins and the kneading troughs and the goat skins for covering and——"

Zichri smiled, proud of his son's spirit. "All right," he said, "go ahead. Do as you have said."

Then Jachin asked, "What shall I do?"

"You may take down the tent and gather up the cooking pots and the stones."

"Right," Jachin answered with spirit, seeming suddenly to wake up.

"Each to his task," Zichri commanded. The men scattered in different directions. The plan was that if any guards met them they would appear to be finishing some work.

Abi ran down the lines filling up all the water skins. Jachin followed him with skins for covering and for cooking pots.

Abi folded the tents. Jachin pulled out all the stakes and wound up the ropes.

After an hour or two the work was stopped in order to allow time for the guards to fall asleep. A little later Zichri went down the lines to see that all was ready. The camels were well laden. There was food, water, as much as could be carried, and weapons.

"Father," Abihu called, "I'll just run over to say goodbye to Mamma."

"No," his father answered sternly. "If we do that we shall never leave Egypt. The women wouldn't let us go. No farewells, and no tears! If you want to march on to freedom you must act like a man."

Abi's eyes filled with tears in spite of himself. But he bit his lips and said, "Yes, Father."

The slaves began to slip away quietly. Behind the camels, between the tents, even at the risk of being killed by some guard, they took their way. At the appointed hour they all lined up silently, beyond the guard line.

Zichri then gave the command, "March on!" These brave, liberty-loving men started their long march for freedom.

> March—march—march
> Over hill and over sand,
> The iron men are marching
> To the free—the Promised Land.

*   *   *

The sun rose in the sky and beat down on the marchers. They stopped only to give some water to the camels. For themselves —not even a drink. They would bear up without food or drink as long as possible. By evening they had covered quite a long distance. If the Egyptians should try to pursue them they would not know which way to turn. The Jewish slaves did not cross the sea. They marched northward into the Sinai desert.

As the sun was setting behind the mountains Zichri ordered the men to camp for the night. Abi drove the stakes for the tent into the ground. Together with Jachin he stretched the ropes. They spread out the rugs and the goat skins for covering. Jachin then stretched himself out and was asleep even before he could eat the cheese and thin cakes of bread which Zichri had laid aside for the children only.

Abi was eating his portion as the men gathered around the camp fire. His father, as usual, was telling the men about their forefathers and their great past.

As Abi was falling asleep he heard his father say: "We are not the first and we are not the last generation of men who have tried to flee from slavery. Many before us have done the same. Many will follow after us. Some of us may reach the Promised Land; others may die in the desert."

That was all Abi heard. He was fast asleep. After only a few hours' sleep the camp was awakened. While it was still dark the tents were taken down, and the caravan again took up the march. Zichri led the way, holding aloft a burning torch. And thus for weeks the march continued.

But the food was getting low. Some of the men had blisters on their feet. Others had died of the great heat. They were hungry and thirsty and sick. It was hard, this march to freedom.

Some men grumbled: "After all, we did have fresh onions and cucumbers in Egypt. Perhaps it was wrong for us to have left Egypt. We won't reach the Promised Land. We'll just die in the desert."

But who were those figures in the distance? Riding on wild horses, they were coming out from behind the rocks, the wild men of the desert!

The Jewish slaves, the hungry, the thirsty, the blistered—all prepared for battle.

"To arms," Zichri commanded. They took up their knives, spears, swords—and rocks if they had nothing else. The battle was a fierce one. Many were killed in the desert.

They could not stop to dig graves for the dead. Their bodies were just left lying on the desert sands. And the caravan marched on. With parched tongues, blistered feet, their arrows gone, their spears broken, they kept marching. Like men of steel they marched on.

Months passed. Abi's and Jachin's hair, like that of the others, had grown long and shaggy. Their clothes were nothing but rags. Every day more men were left dead on the desert sands.

At last Zichri, too, died. But Abi did not cry. He remembered his father's command, "No tears!"

A year passed. Abi and Jachin were now alone in the desert —alone on the hot, dry sands. Abi wasn't afraid. The dead men around him had been brave and true men whom he had loved and respected.

Until that moment Jachin had been brave. But now things seemed different. As the children sat silently in the silent desert, Jachin suddenly asked, "How about turning back, Abi?"

"Turning back!" Abi exclaimed, amazed at the question.

"Yes. We have no food. We can't fight these wild men of the desert by ourselves."

As Jachin spoke they heard a flapping of wings overhead, and a shadow appeared on the ground. A big eagle was making circles in the air. Then suddenly he swooped down toward the dead men. Jachin hid his head in his hands. Through his parted fingers he could see the curved claws of the eagle. "At any moment," he thought, "this eagle will carry me off into the air."

The eagle flew low over the bodies. Their faces looked so strong, so fearless, so brave, that it seemed as if even in death they could defend themselves. The eagle hesitated a moment, as if frightened by the strength of the sleeping heroes. Then suddenly he soared into the air.

Jachin huddled closer to Abihu. "He's coming down on me. I feel him coming toward me." Jachin screamed and crouched low. "He has a hold on my neck! Help!"

But Abi saw that it was only a feather which had dropped from the eagle. "Look, silly! It's only a feather," he laughed, "only a feather dropped by the eagle in his flight!"

Jachin breathed more freely and smiled weakly. Again they sat listening to the desert silence.

"For miles upon miles all around,—
Not a voice,—not a murmur,—no sound,"

Abi began to recite.

"We were talking about food. Tell me, what shall we eat?" Jachin interrupted him.

"We can eat the juices from the tamarisk trees."

"Where are the trees, Abi?" Jachin asked, looking into the wild desert stretching ahead of him.

"Oh, don't worry. We'll find them," Abi comforted him.

But his mind was not on his words, for his eyes were fixed on a huge serpent which was coming slowly toward him. "Before this," Abi thought, "we never noticed these things."

Suddenly the serpent stretched himself out to his full length, so that he lay within reach of the dead bodies.

"What's this?" he seemed to ask as he slowly reared his head higher and higher. The eyes of the serpent glared green. Then, cutting the air like a knife came the sudden HISS—HISS of the serpent.

And now a strange thing happened. Just as the snake was ready to strike he suddenly recoiled. Had he, too, been frightened by the glory that surrounded the faces of the heroes sleeping there?

Abi was startled this time.

Now it was Jachin's turn to act the hero.

"Look, Abi, look at the quick, graceful movements of that serpent! Don't be a coward! It's only a lively little serpent. Go pull it back by its tail. It will make a nice toy!" Jachin teased, as the serpent glided silently back into the crevice from which he had come.

Thirsty and worn by fear, the children spread their mats on the ground. The sun was setting behind the hills. The air was getting chilly. Abi pulled the goat skins over Jachin and himself, and they both fell sound asleep.

When they awoke it was night. The sun had already gone down behind the hills. A pale silvery moon had come up in the sky. The children arose, folded their mats and skins and began silently to pick their way among the dead men. Their broken swords and spears sparkled in the moonlight.

As the boys hurried along, almost afraid to breathe, there was a sudden cry from the jackals. And that was answered by the hooting of an owl. Then out of nowhere came the mighty roar of a lion. He seemed to be coming closer. He was roaring louder now.

Then began the symphony of the desert. The asses brayed, the jackals screamed, the owls hooted and above them all,— loud as a trumpet call, sounded the lion's roar.

Abi and Jachin moved closer to each other. "Isn't this enough to wake the dead?" they asked each other.

But the mighty heroes lay silent. Not a hair nor an eyelid stirred. Even the lion stopped roaring when he saw them. He stood still in his tracks as if awed by the mighty heroes asleep.

"I'm tired and scared," Jachin began to cry. "I can't walk any more."

"You're just hungry. Wait here and I'll go to look for some birds' eggs and jellied juices from the—" His voice died out in the distance. On his return he found Jachin asleep. Tired and discouraged, he, too, went to sleep.

A rolling, shattering thunder shook the desert. The lightning flashed over rocks and hills. The wind howled.

Abi woke up. He began to tremble with fear. Gone was the desert silence. Were the mighty heroes stirring? Their eyes seemed to flash fire, their faces aflame.

Had he been sleeping an hour or a year, Abi wondered.

"Who are all these?" He didn't seem to recognize them.

Surely there were more men there than had come with his father from Egypt. Then he recalled his father's talk at the camp-fire.

"Oh, of course, these are those great heroes, those giants of long ago who went forth to cast off their yoke of slavery."

As Abi was thinking the men seemed to rise up tall, like giants, and thousands of them thundered forth in chorus:

> Warriors are we,
> Last in slavery,
> First to be free.
> To arms—
> In lines—fall in;
> We advance in a band
> To the Promised Land.

At the tremendous roar of the chorus, Jachin awakened too. He looked into Abi's terrified face.

"What's happening?" he called wildly. "Who are all these men? Where did they come from?"

No sooner had Jachin put the question than the storm quieted down. The thunder stopped, the lightning ceased. The desert lay calm in the moonlight. Again, just as before, the dead lay, mighty in their silence.

"Hurry, Abi, let's get away from here!" Jachin shrieked.

Even the brave Abi was weakening. "Yes, we'll go. Only

wait a moment and I will take a girdle from one of these dead giants—just to remember the example of these mighty heroes."

Jachin did not wait. He ran back in the direction of Egypt. Abi was calling, "Wait, I'm coming, I'm coming—but we're not going that way. We're going onward to the Promised Land."

"Did you forget?" he called to Jachin as he arose from the ground.

But, behold! What had happened? Try as he would, he could not move! "Jachin, Jachin," Abi cried, distressed. "I can't move. I can go neither forward nor backward."

On hearing this Jachin quickly ran back to his cousin. He took hold of Abi's arm and pulled with all his might, but Abi remained rooted to the spot.

Suddenly Jachin said, "Give me that girdle you took from the dead man. Maybe that will help. I'll tie it around you and pull."

Abi handed Jachin the belt. No sooner was the belt out of his hand than his feet loosened. To make sure, he lifted his right foot. Sure enough, he could step forward. Come on, Jachin, we'll both go now," he said, excitedly, as he kicked his feet.

But Jachin, pale as a ghost, stood holding the girdle in his hands. He stood fixed to the spot, shrieking, "I can't move, I can't move."

"Drop the girdle! Drop it!" Abi called. Jachin was too scared to understand. "Just throw it down on the ground," Abi cried as he swung his arms downward. At last Jachin dropped

the belt, and behold, immediately he felt as if chains had been lifted from his feet.

"Let's run," said Abi. "They will not let us remove anything from these dead bodies—but keep only their memory! Let's get out of the desert!"

* * *

"Get out of the desert! Get out of the desert! But how? How?" Bialik repeated, half awake, as his wife shook him.

"Chaim, don't you feel well? Mr. Ravnitsky and the others from the publishing house are waiting for you, but I just couldn't wake you up!"

Bialik opened his blue eyes and looked at his wife.

"I guess it was all a dream! But it will make a beautiful poem! I'll just jot down the idea. Then I'll write the poem some other time. You know, it takes me a long time to write a good line."

And Chaim Nachman Bialik took a pencil and wrote the idea of the poem: "The Jews must break the yoke. They must get out of the desert. They must become free men, free men in the Promised Land."

UNION GRADED SERIES

EDITED BY

EMANUEL GAMORAN, PH.D., *Director of Education*
Union of American Hebrew Congregations